# PERCENTAGE DEPLETION

## ECONOMIC PROGRESS AND

## NATIONAL SECURITY

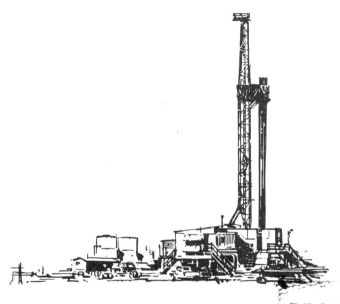

Prepared by a

SPECIAL TASK FORCE

comprised of members of the
Mid-Continent Oil & Gas Association

Published by the
Mid-Continent Oil & Gas Association

Tulsa, Oklahoma

March, 1968

# PERCENTAGE DEPLETION, ECONOMIC PROGRESS AND NATIONAL SECURITY

## TABLE OF CONTENTS

Foreword . . . . . . . . . . . . . . . . . . . . . . . . . . . . . . . . . . . . . . . . . . . . iii
1. Introduction . . . . . . . . . . . . . . . . . . . . . . . . . . . . . . . . . . . . . . 1
2. Importance of Oil to Economic Progress
  Correlation of Standard of Living with Consumption of
    Energy . . . . . . . . . . . . . . . . . . . . . . . . . . . . . . . . . . . . . . . . 5
  Advantages of Petroleum as a Source of Energy . . . . . . . . . . 9
  Future Demand and Supply . . . . . . . . . . . . . . . . . . . . . . . . . . 11
3. Importance of Oil to National Security
  Petroleum in Possible Future Wars . . . . . . . . . . . . . . . . . . . 16
  Petroleum and the Cold War . . . . . . . . . . . . . . . . . . . . . . . . 19
4. Risks in This Extractive Industry
  Nature of the Petroleum Industry . . . . . . . . . . . . . . . . . . . . 23
  Discovery Record . . . . . . . . . . . . . . . . . . . . . . . . . . . . . . . . . 26
  Capital Requirements . . . . . . . . . . . . . . . . . . . . . . . . . . . . . . 28
5. The Recovery of Capital Value
  Early Depletion Legislation . . . . . . . . . . . . . . . . . . . . . . . . . 31
  The Discovery Value Principle . . . . . . . . . . . . . . . . . . . . . . . 32
  Adoption of Percentage Depletion . . . . . . . . . . . . . . . . . . . . 33
  The Capital Gain Alternative . . . . . . . . . . . . . . . . . . . . . . . . 34
6. Prices, Profits and Taxes
  Prices of Petroleum Products . . . . . . . . . . . . . . . . . . . . . . . . 36
  Profits of the Oil Industry . . . . . . . . . . . . . . . . . . . . . . . . . . 40
  Oil Industry's Tax Burden . . . . . . . . . . . . . . . . . . . . . . . . . . 43
7. Foreign Production and Percentage Depletion
  Taxation of Income from Foreign Production . . . . . . . . . . . . 46
  Effect on U. S. Tax Revenues of a Change in Foreign
    Depletion . . . . . . . . . . . . . . . . . . . . . . . . . . . . . . . . . . . . . . 48
  Foreign Crude Oil and National Security . . . . . . . . . . . . . . 49
  Impact of U.S. Balance of Payments . . . . . . . . . . . . . . . . . . 49
  Aid to Friendly Nations . . . . . . . . . . . . . . . . . . . . . . . . . . . . 50
8. Conclusion . . . . . . . . . . . . . . . . . . . . . . . . . . . . . . . . . . . . . . . 52
  Appendix A — Analysis of Criticisms Against Percentage De-
    pletion . . . . . . . . . . . . . . . . . . . . . . . . . . . . . . . . . . . . . . . 56
  Appendix B — Legislative History of Percentage Depletion for
    Oil and Gas Production . . . . . . . . . . . . . . . . . . . . . . . . . 72

# Foreword

In these days of global tensions, we hear a great deal about the importance of America's keeping abreast or ahead of the totalitarian nations in such fields as industrial productivity, missile development, and space exploration. It is surprising, however, that so little attention is paid to America's lead in one of the most crucial races of all: the use and availability of energy resources.

Without abundant supplies of energy, we could not for long maintain the industrial complex and the military strength so vital to our country's future. Both our economic progress and our national security are inseparably linked to our energy resources.

The practical effect of the percentage depletion provisions in our tax laws has been to make available more oil and gas at lower prices than would otherwise prevail.

That is why every American citizen has such a tremendous stake in percentage depletion. Oil and gas currently provide nearly three-fourths of the nation's energy. The Defense Department and the Department of the Interior have said that, for at least the remainder of this century, hydrocarbons will continue to supply the bulk of our energy requirements. With percentage depletion, as it now exists, we have the assurance of experience that the United States will continue to hold its traditional energy supremacy.

For over four decades, percentage depletion has served as a powerful incentive for the discovery and development of petroleum supplies. At the same time, it has recognized the unusual nature of the risks involved. It has been a most important factor in accomplishing what Congress intended it should accomplish—namely, the discovery and development of adequate petroleum reserves—and the entire nation has reaped the benefits.

Today, when our energy needs are greater than ever and still growing, it would be a serious mistake to tamper with percentage depletion. Experience has proved that the present rate is no more than enough to stimulate the kind of finding and development effort that the nation requires. It has simultaneously kept prices to consumers at a very reasonable level. As one slogan has it: "Gasoline's a buy. Only the tax is high." In fact, the tax burden borne by the oil industry, even excluding excise taxes on products, is comparable to that borne by other industries. Finally, the profits of oil companies have been in line with those of industry generally.

The purpose of this booklet is to present the basic facts that show percentage depletion always has been—and is now—in the public interest. It has been tested by time and should be maintained. To undercut percentage depletion—the key to abundant energy for a strong America—would be a reckless gamble with the nation's progress and security.

# 1

# INTRODUCTION

The percentage depletion provisions in our federal income tax law permit producers of over a hundred different kinds of minerals to deduct a percentage of their gross income from each producing property in computing taxable income. For producers of oil and gas, the deduction allowed is 27½ per cent of the value at the well of crude oil and gas produced. The deduction for each property is limited, however, to 50 per cent of the net income from the property before deducting depletion.

Stripped of numerous complications, the following two examples demonstrate how percentage depletion works. If in a given year a property produces crude oil worth $10,000 at the wellhead, and production costs are $4,000, the percentage depletion deduction for this property would be 27½ per cent of $10,000 or $2,750. In this case taxable income would be determined as follows:

| | |
|---|---|
| Gross Income | $10,000 |
| Less—Production Costs | 4,000 |
| Income Before Depletion and Before Income Tax | $ 6,000 |
| Less—Depletion Deduction | 2,750 |
| Taxable Income | $ 3,250 |

If production costs were $6,000 instead of $4,000, the percentage depletion deduction would be limited to $2,000 because it may not in any event exceed 50 per cent of the net income from the property. Under these conditions, the computation of taxable income would be as follows:

| | |
|---|---:|
| Gross Income | $10,000 |
| Less—Production Costs | 6,000 |
| Income Before Depletion and Before Income Tax | $ 4,000 |
| Less—Depletion Deduction (limited to 50 per cent of $4,000) | 2,000 |
| Taxable Income | $ 2,000 |

The fact that the depletion deduction can in no event exceed 50 percent of net income from any property precludes the possibility that percentage depletion could ever eliminate all tax liability. The most that percentage depletion can do with respect to any mineral is to cause the income from production to be taxed at about the same effective rate as would apply to capital gains.

It should be noted that percentage depletion is not allowed on income attributable to transportation, refining, or marketing operations since, for depletion purposes, gross income is restricted to the value at the wellhead of the crude oil and natural gas produced.

Percentage depletion was first adopted in the law in 1926 as a substitute for depletion based on "discovery value." Discovery value depletion had been adopted in 1918 as an incentive to find new oil supplies that were needed in World War I. This provision allowed a depletion deduction based on the value of oil and gas in the ground at the time of discovery, thus placing new properties on an equal basis with those discovered before March 1, 1913. It proved difficult to administer, however, because of endless controversies between taxpayers and the government over values. To avoid these controversies and to simplify administration,

Congress adopted the percentage depletion formula in 1926. The Treasury Department made a study that indicated a rate of more than 30 per cent would be required to provide results equivalent to the discovery value deductions, but the rate of 27½ per cent was adopted as a compromise between differing House and Senate proposals.

The fact that percentage depletion has passed so many searching examinations and has been extended to other industries testifies to its soundness. This provision has proved itself in practice and has become an integral part of the economics of the petroleum and other extractive industries. By recognizing the special nature of the oil producing industry, percentage depletion has enabled the industry to meet our nation's constantly increasing peacetime petroleum requirements and extraordinary needs in time of war.

# 2

# Importance of Oil to Economic Progress

In this country of ours, progress is sometimes taken for granted. But progress—especially economic progress—is far from inevitable. Whether a nation moves forward or lags behind depends largely on the way its people direct the forces that control its material welfare.

Many forces can exert a favorable influence on a nation's economy; among the major ones are freedom, education, machines, and energy. Freedom and education are of great importance, but they must be coupled with machines and energy before man can reach the maximum potential of his productive efforts. Without machines, and without abundant supplies of low-cost energy to power these machines, a nation cannot maintain a strong economy in this industrialized world.

During the last 100 years, the United States has made great strides in multiplying production, easing the burden of work, and raising the standard of living. Our economic progress has been truly phenomenal, and oil and gas have made vital and indispensable contributions to this progress. They have become our principal sources of energy.

America is unique in its extensive use of these fuels. Our consumption of petroleum is about 40 percent of the total of the free world. Among the highly industralized nations of the free world, the United States and Canada are unique in having the capacity to produce enough petroleum from domestic resources to meet present domestic requirements.

With our tremendous stake in oil and gas as sources of energy, and with our need for these fuels continuing to grow, it seems clear that our national policies—including those relating to taxation—should be designed to encourage the maximum economic development of our petroleum resources. Only in this way will it be possible to provide adequate supplies of oil and gas for our expanding economy.

## Correlation of Standard of Living With Consumption of Energy

America's unexcelled productivity is the result of a "high-energy civilization." Our standard of living is closely related to our high consumption of energy and to the substitution of inanimate energy—chiefly mineral—for the work previously done (and still being done in the world's poorer areas) by humans and animals. In this country, since 1850, the per capita use of energy to provide motive power for work performance has increased sixfold. In 1850, animals and humans provided 65 per cent of all the energy consumed in the United States. By 1950, more than 98 per cent was inanimate.[1]

A reduction of more than 40 per cent in the average work week was made possible by our high per capita use of energy over the past century. At the same time, the real weekly income per worker has increased more than 300 per cent.

The relation between energy consumption and economic welfare is not uniform among countries because of climatic, occupational, and other variations. In spite of these dif-

[1]Dewhurst, *America's Needs and Resources*, p. 908.

ferences, however, there is an obvious correlation between per capita energy consumption and per capita income. As Figure 1 shows, the countries with high per capita consumption of energy are those with high productivity and a high standard of living, while low energy consumption is characteristic of low productivity and low standards of living. For example, consumption of mineral energy in America in 1965 was the equivalent of 1,912 gallons of crude oil for each person compared with 203 gallons for residents of Mexico. This difference in energy consumption is reflected in national incomes, with the United States having $2,894 per capita and Mexico only $412 per capita in 1965.[2] The relationship between energy consumption and real gross national product per capita in the United States from 1929 to 1966 is graphically illustrated in Figure 2.

Admiral H. G. Rickover once commented that the mineral energy consumed in the United States feeds machines which make each of us master of an army of mechanical slaves.

> Man's muscle power is rated at 35 watts continuously, or one-twentieth horsepower. Machines therefore furnish every American industrial worker with energy equivalent to that of 244 men, while at least 2,000 men push his automobile along the road, and his family is supplied with 33 faithful household helpers. Each locomotive engineer controls energy equivalent to that of 100,000 men; each jet pilot of 700,000 men. Truly, the humblest American enjoys the services of more slaves than were once owned by the richest nobles, and lives better than most ancient kings.[3]

Coal was the primary fuel of the Industrial Revolution from its beginning in the eighteenth century through the

[2]United Nations, *Statistical Yearbook*, 1966, pp. 78-86, 344-347, 550-553, and 578-582. (Conversion based on 209 gallons of crude being equal to a ton of coal.)
[3]Admiral H. G. Rickover, USN, "Energy Resources and Our Future," paper presented May 14, 1957, before the Annual Scientific Assembly of the Minnesota State Medical Association.

# FIGURE 1

## ENERGY CONSUMPTION AND INCOME ARE CLOSELY RELATED

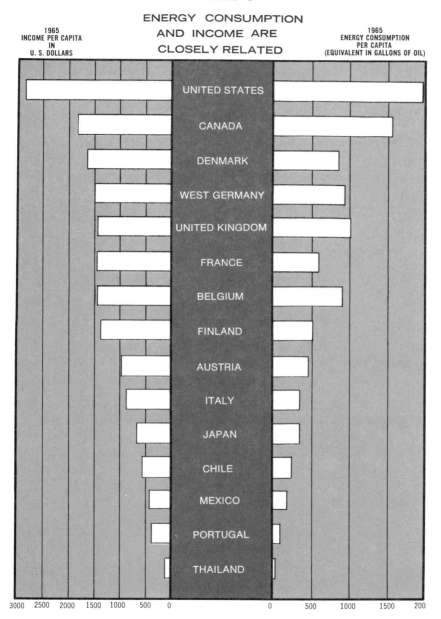

1965 INCOME PER CAPITA IN U. S. DOLLARS

1965 ENERGY CONSUMPTION PER CAPITA (EQUIVALENT IN GALLONS OF OIL)

UNITED STATES
CANADA
DENMARK
WEST GERMANY
UNITED KINGDOM
FRANCE
BELGIUM
FINLAND
AUSTRIA
ITALY
JAPAN
CHILE
MEXICO
PORTUGAL
THAILAND

3000  2500  2000  1500  1000  500  0        0  500  1000  1500  200

Source: Computed from data published by United Nations, Statistical Yearbook—1966

FIGURE 2

ENERGY CONSUMPTION AND REAL GROSS NATIONAL
PRODUCT PER CAPITA ARE CLOSELY RELATED—

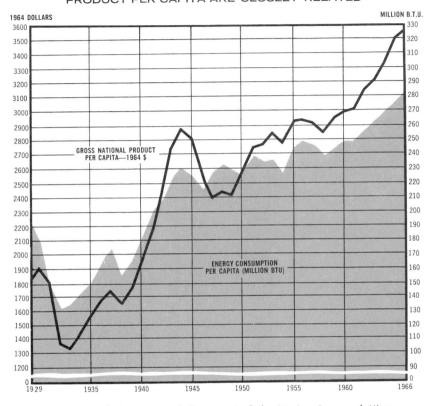

Source: Department of Commerce and Department of the Interior, Bureau of Mines

nineteenth century and until the extraordinary development of oil and gas in the United States in the twentieth century. As indicated in Figure 3, petroleum has grown in importance until it now provides almost three-fourths of the total energy consumed in the United States.

It is significant that the rise in consumption of petroleum and natural gas in the United States since 1920 is greater than the rise in total use of energy. Oil and gas

FIGURE 3

PERCENTAGE OF ENERGY CONSUMPTION
IN THE UNITED STATES

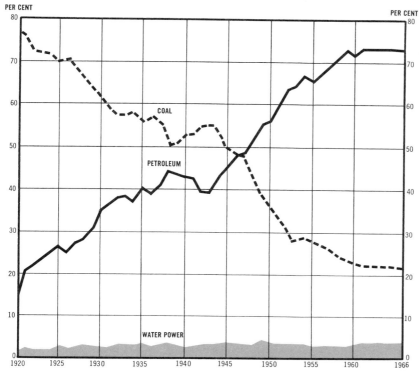

Source: *Petroleum facts and figures, Centennial Edition, 1959, p. 368, and 1965 Edition,
p. 235. Data for 1964, 1965, and 1966 from Department of the Interior, Bureau
of Mines.*

provided 3,503 trillion BTUs in 1920, 41,819 trillion
in 1966. This increase of 38,316 trillion BTUs was more
than the increase in total energy from all sources during that
period.[4]

## Advantages of Petroleum as a Source of Energy

As it comes from the earth, crude oil is a mixture of thou-

[4]United States Department of the Interior, Bureau of Mines, *Crude Petroleum and
Petroleum Products*, 1962 and 1966, Supplement Table 4.

sands of different hydrocarbon compounds. All of them can be burned virtually without residue, which is why crude oil is such a wonderful source of fuel. Crude oil is also the source of nearly all of our lubricants, without which our highly mechanized economy could not function.

In the various refinery processes, crude oil is broken up into its component parts, or fractions, which then are manufactured into finished products. There is a minimum of labor required in refining crude oil, and there are virtually no waste products. About 85 per cent of the finished products represents gasoline and other liquid fuels, all of which can be efficiently converted to energy, while the balance consists of non-fuel products, such as asphalt, lubricating oil, rubber, and petrochemicals.

The steadily increasing importance of oil and natural gas in our economy is traceable primarily to their high ratio of usable energy to weight and bulk and to the ease of transportation, convenience, and cleanness in handling and combustion. With the internal combustion engine predominant in transportation, liquid fuels are indispensable since their function cannot be served by other forms of energy. Oil operations have, therefore, been geared largely to supplying the demand for gasoline, but modern refining processes yield many other important products which are available to consumers at attractive prices, not only for transportation, but also for home heating, industrial uses, and many other purposes. No other fuel can match petroleum in its flexibility and wide variety of application. Petroleum products, in short, make possible a degree of mechanization and an economic efficiency not otherwise available.

Not only is petroleum a source of fuel and power; more than a thousand products directly or indirectly derived from it are employed in the home and industry. Of these products, four groups are outstanding: detergents, synthetic rubber, synthetic fibers, and plastics. The development of an adequate supply of synthetic rubber by the petroleum industry at a critical time in World War II has substantially freed us from dependence on foreign supplies of natural rubber. In addition, many of the raw materials used today in the synthesis of organic chemicals are derived from petroleum. More than 68 per cent of all synthetic organic chemicals manufactured in the U. S. is derived from petroleum.[5] This is true despite the fact that less than two per cent of all petroleum is used for this purpose.

## Future Demand and Supply

It is sometimes suggested that the development of atomic energy will soon reduce the importance of other sources of energy and that great volumes of petroleum will not be needed in the future. Eventually, the demand for petroleum energy may decline but such a change is likely to be a great many years in the future. It has been over twenty years since the advent of atomic energy, but in spite of the billions of dollars spent on atomic research and development, only a tenth of one per cent of the United States' energy supply comes from nuclear or atomic sources.[6]

The Department of the Interior anticipates that in 1980 nuclear energy will provide only 2.4 per cent of the total energy consumption in the United States.[7] The Atomic Energy Commission informed President Kennedy that the impact of nuclear power would be "quite small" during the next 20 years and estimated that by 1980 nuclear energy would account for only about 3 per cent of domestic energy

[5]United States Department of the Interior, *An Appraisal of the Petroleum Industry of the United States,* January, 1965, p. v.
[6]American Petroleum Institute, *Petroleum Facts and Figures,* 1965 Edition, p. 235.
[7]United States Department of the Interior, *Supplies, Costs, and Uses of the Fossil Fuels,* February, 1963, Table 24.

requirements.[8] Finally, the National Power Survey, published by the Federal Power Commission, estimated that almost 6 per cent of the 1980 domestic energy consumption would come from nuclear sources.[9]

It is clear that for the foreseeable future the bulk of the nation's energy supply will be met by fossil fuels, primarily in the form of petroleum. In fact, the Department of the Interior predicts that liquid petroleum consumption in 1980 will be 17.6 million barrels a day, an increase of 47 per cent over 1966.[10]

With future requirements for petroleum looming so large, the adequacy of supply becomes of paramount importance. In the past, the domestic oil industry has increased reserves and producing capacity as required to meet increases in demand. On December 31, 1946, proved recoverable liquid petroleum reserves in the United States were estimated to be 24 billion barrels, or about twelve times the 1946 production. Over the following twenty years, 54 billion barrels were produced (a figure more than twice the 1946 reserves), and yet, proved reserves on January 1, 1967, were 40 billion barrels. During this period of rapidly rising consumption, the domestic oil industry had found 70 billion barrels of new reserves.[11]

In the 13 years beginning in 1968, it is anticipated that production will be 55 billion barrels. This means that additions to reserves must total 75 billion barrels in order to maintain reserves at 12 times annual production:[12]

[8]United States Atomic Energy Commission, Appendices to *Civilian Nuclear Power . . . A Report to the President*, 1962, pp. 69-70.

[9]United States Federal Power Commission, *National Power Survey*, 1964, Part I, pp. 37 and 53.

[10]United States Department of the Interior, *An Appraisal of the Petroleum Industry of the United States*, January, 1965, p. 18.

[11]American Gas Association, American Petroleum Institute, and Canadian Petroleum Association, *Reserves of Crude Oil, Natural Gas Liquids, and Natural Gas in the U. S. and Canada as of Decmber 31, 1966*, July, 1967.

[12]Determined from data derived from *An Appraisal of the Petroleum Industry of the United States*, op. cit., pp. 18 and 19, and *Reserves of Crude Oil, Natural Gas Liquids, and Natural Gas in the U. S. and Canada*, op. cit., pp. 13 and 255.

|  | Liquid Hydrocarbons (Billion Barrels) |
|---|---|
| Anticipated Production, 1968-1980 ............ | 55 |
| Proved Reserves at 12/31/80 (12 times estimated production in 1980) ............... | 60 |
| Total ................................. | 115 |
| Less—Proved Reserves at 12/31/67 ............ | 40 |
| Required Additions to Reserves, 1968-1980 ...... | 75 |

The need to find 75 billion barrels of new reserves in the next 13 years seems a most challenging objective when one considers that cumulative production since the Drake well in 1859 has been about 90 billion barrels.

Through improved technology it is now possible to produce more than one-twelfth of our reserves annually without waste. It may be that annual production rates of one-ninth of reserves may be feasible within the next few years. In this event, reserves of 45 billion barrels might be adequate for 1980 and discoveries during the period from 1968 to 1980 will need to be only 60 billion barrels. Since additions to reserves during the past ten years have averaged 3.4 billion barrels a year, it is clear that efforts to find new reserves will have to be stepped up to meet the needs forecast through 1980.

Such forecasts pose the question: Is it likely that new oil reserves of this magnitude will be found even if exploration efforts are stepped up? The best estimates available indicate that ultimate discoveries may be adequate to satisfy our needs for many years to come. In 1964, the United States Geological Survey concluded that a total of 300 billion barrels, exclusive of the then proved reserves, may be a reasonable figure for the ultimate reserves of the United States and of the adjoining continental shelves, considering significant improvements in recoverability that are now being acomplished or promised in the future.[13] A survey by the staff of the *Oil and Gas Journal* in 1958 showed that several major oil companies estimated the nation's ultimate reserves of crude oil to be about 300 billion barrels or more.[14] All such estimates are speculative. Historically, estimates of future demands for petroleum and estimates of future discoveries have tended to be low. It may be, therefore, that the latest estimates are also too low.

It appears, then, that the future supply of oil and gas in the United States will be determined by two major factors: the technology of finding and developing reserves and the economic incentives for capital investment. The technology of finding and producing oil has improved dramatically through the years, and the quantities of oil to be found in America seem to be adequate for foreseeable needs. But in the last analysis it is capital that converts natural resources into available supplies. The cost of finding and developing new petroleum reserves is constantly increasing, and, as petroleum requirements are also increasing, the oil industry will have to invest progressively greater amounts of money to meet the nation's needs. Continuation of the percentage depletion incentive will be essential to attract the investment and reinvestment of the amounts of money needed.

---

[13] *An Appraisal of the Petroleum Industry of the United States*, op. cit., p. 15.
[14] *Oil and Gas Journal*, Vol. 56, No. 20, May 19, 1958, p. 114.

# 3

# Importance of Oil
## to National Security

It has long been recognized that an adequate supply of oil and gas is essential to our national security. Petroleum provides the fuel for airplanes, tanks, ships, and other military vehicles; constitutes the basic ingredient of conventional explosives; and provides the energy for the industrial might on which America's military strength is based. The vital role of petroleum products was clearly demonstrated in both World Wars I and II.[15] In other emergencies, such as the Korean War, Viet Nam, and Middle East Crises in 1956 and 1967, adequate supplies of petroleum produced by American companies have again proved essential to our security. On the other hand, during World War II fuel shortages grounded much of the German air force during crucial periods and seriously curtailed the effectiveness of Hitler's ground forces. But the support given to the allies by the American petroleum industry left nothing to be desired. Shortly after the end of the war, the Joint Chiefs of Staff of the Army-Navy Petroleum Board offered the following tribute to the industry:

> . . . The urgent demand of the Army and Navy for unprecedented volumes of aviation gasoline, motor gasoline, diesel oil, fuel oils, lubricants and countless other petroleum prod-

[15]In World War II, more than one-half of all the tonnage shipped from the U. S. to our military forces consisted of petroleum products. See *Petroleum in War and Peace*, papers presented by Petroleum Administration for War before Senate Special Committee to Investigate Petroleum Resources, "Oil in Peace and War," Ralph K. Davies, p. 6.

ucts vital to victory were unending and often appeared impossible of fulfillment.

It is a very special tribute, therefore, that at no time did the services lack for oil in the proper quantities, in the proper kinds, and at the proper places.

## Petroleum in Possible Future Wars

Predictions of petroleum requirements in a future war entail a great deal of speculation. However, it would be folly for us to risk having an inadequate supply. Even with the development of nuclear weapons, petroleum continues to be necessary for our military strength. Since we wish to avoid the massive destruction of nuclear warfare, we must be prepared to fight effectively by conventional methods.

In testimony before the Committee on Ways and Means on March 26, 1963, General Lucius D. Clay expressed the opinion that, if an all-out nuclear war should come, it would most likely escalate from a conventional attack and conventional defense. General Clay believed that the greatest risk of a nuclear war would occur if a nuclear power involved in a conventional war should find its defense inadequate.[16] He contended, therefore, that it is absolutely essential that we be prepared to carry on successfully a conventional or limited war as a means of preventing a nuclear war. The validity of General Clay's opinions is generally accepted because most of the principal nations in the Free World today, including the United States, have larger conventional military forces than ever before in times of peace.

If a nuclear war should occur, it would probably be over in a short time, in which event a great volume of petroleum would not be required for actual military operations. Petroleum energy, however, would be of paramount importance in the ordeal of recovery and rebuilding. We would be com-

[16]Hearings Before the Committee on Ways and Means, 88th Congress, First Session, on the Tax Recommendations of the President Contained in His Message Transmitted to Congress January 24, 1963, Part 7, p. 3674.

pletely dependent on our petroleum powered transportation systems during this period. After the critical recovery period, an adequate supply of energy would be as important as ever before in developing a new industrial economy.

Thus the importance of an adequate supply of petroleum in event of either a conventional war or a nuclear war cannot be questioned. Although an adequate domestic supply is of primary importance, it also strengthens our defenses to have oil resources in many other parts of the world. In both world wars the availability of foreign oil contributed significantly to achieving our objectives. In each emergency a large part of the oil consumed came from foreign sources. Oil from many parts of the globe shortened supply lines and increased the effectiveness of military operations.

During the period since World War II our participation in the development of foreign sources of oil reduced the risk of war. If this oil were developed solely by the militarily weaker nations, the Iron Curtain countries would make every effort to obtain control. Such efforts would endanger the peace, particularly where defense commitments have been made by the United States.

Our supplies of foreign oil also contributed significantly to the maintenance of Free World security and the avoidance of the possible outbreak of a general war, during both the Suez crisis of 1956 and the Arab-Israeli conflict of 1967. Even in 1956 the economies of Western Europe had become highly dependent upon Middle Eastern crude for normal supplies. The Suez crisis cut off these supplies and the threat of fuel deprivation forced England and France to undertake belligerent action which could have led to a total war. But with reserve supplies in Venezuela and also in domestic fields, the United States was in a position to supply all Western European energy needs and exert its influence to maintain world peace. Had the United States itself been dependent upon Middle Eastern oil, such a measure of restraint would have been impossible and war might have resulted. The same situation recurred in the 1967 crisis, at which time Western Europe had become even more completely dependent upon imported oil; and the dangers of war would have been correspondingly greater had the United States not possessed spare productive capacity in both foreign and domestic fields.

It must be concluded that the availability of an adequate supply of petroleum, coupled with widely dispersed sources of petroleum, is essential to our national security. Percentage depletion enables American firms to provide the petroleum in both the quantities and the localities needed. Thus to the extent percentage depletion is successful, America's defenses are strengthened and the possibilities of preventing hostilities are improved.

## TABLE I

### World Crude Oil Reserves and Production — 1945

| | (Millions of Barrels) | | | |
| | Crude Oil Reserves 1-1-1946 | Production 1945 | Per Cent of World | |
| | | | Reserves | Production |
|---|---|---|---|---|
| United States | 19,942 | 1,737 | 34.4% | 61.8% |
| Canada | 150 | 8 | 0.3 | 0.3 |
| Venezuela | 7,000 | 322 | 12.1 | 11.5 |
| Middle East | 18,500 | 201 | 31.9 | 7.2 |
| Other Free World | 3,756 | 202 | 6.5 | 7.2 |
| Total Free World | 49,348 | 2,470 | 85.2% | 88.0% |
| Russia and Red Bloc | 8,594 | 338 | 14.8 | 12.0 |
| Total World | 57,942 | 2,808 | 100.0% | 100.0% |

Source: U. S. figures from API-AGA, *Proved Reserves of Crude Oil, Natural Gas Liquids, and Natural Gas,* December 31, 1959, p. 12. All other data from *The Oil Weekly,* Vol. 2, May 20, 1946, pages 19 and 29. Totals have been adjusted to reflect differences between API and *The Oil Weekly* in estimated U. S. reserves and production (natural gas liquids not included).

# Petroleum and the Cold War

Since energy is vital to economic progress and national security, it is to be expected that oil should become an important factor in the contest between Communist and Free World nations for power and influence. It has become one of the most significant commodities in the "cold war."

In 1946, the United States had greater crude oil reserves than any other area of the world (see Table 1).

Since 1946, however, the entire complexion of the world's oil supply has drastically changed. Our reserves now represent less than a tenth of the total for the world, but we are still depleting our reserves more rapidly than any other major producing area (see Table 2).

Probably the most striking development since 1946 has been the dominance of the Middle East reserves which now represent almost 60 per cent of the reserves of the world.

## TABLE 2
### World Oil Reserves and Production — 1966

| | (Millions of Barrels) | | | |
| | Oil Reserves 1-1-1967 | Production 1966 | Per Cent of World | |
| | | | Reserves | Production |
|---|---|---|---|---|
| United States | 39,781 | 3,453 | 9.5% | 26.4% |
| Canada | 9,051 | 366 | 2.2 | 2.8 |
| Venezuela | 17,000 | 1,291 | 4.1 | 9.9 |
| Middle East | 249,209 | 3,631 | 59.8 | 27.8 |
| Other Free World | 66,025 | 2,056 | 15.8 | 15.7 |
| Total Free World | 381,066 | 10,797 | 91.4% | 82.6% |
| Russia and Red Bloc | 35,773 | 2,277 | 8.6 | 17.4 |
| Total World | 416,839 | 13,074 | 100.0% | 100.0% |

Source: U. S. and Canadian figures from American Gas Association, American Petroleum Institute, and Canadian Petroleum Association; *Reserves of Crude Oil, Natural Gas Liquids, and Natural Gas in the U.S. and Canada;* July, 1967, pp. 13 and 255. All other data from *The Oil and Gas Journal,* December 25, 1967, pp. 118-119.

Production from the Middle East now exceeds the production of the United States. Although the oil fields of the Middle East are just at Russia's doorstep, they are operated by American companies along with other companies of the Free World. Our position in this area is extremely important to the United States in maintaining its influence throughout the world.

The impressive development of the Russian oil industry has provided the Communists a powerful weapon in working toward their ultimate political and economic goals. The National Petroleum Council has pointed out that in 1950 Russia was producing crude oil at the rate of only 760,000 barrels a day. Russia's 1965 production was estimated at 4,900,000 barrels a day, and by 1970, it is expected to exceed 7 million barrels a day.[17]

Most of Russia's energy is derived from sources other than petroleum, and one of the principal objectives in developing its petroleum industry is to provide oil for export. This gives Russia foreign exchange that is needed for the purchase of western technology in the form of industrial plants and equipment, and it creates an opportunity to further the political objectives of the Communists. In 1955, Soviet Bloc oil exports to the Free World amounted to 116,000 barrels a day, but by 1965, they amounted to almost 867,000 barrels a day. The National Petroleum Council estimates that by 1970, Russia will have a crude oil surplus available for export to the Free World of 1,300,000 to 1,-600,000 barrels a day.[18]

Because it aims to curb U. S. trade, disrupt the flow of world commerce, and increase its influence on other Free World nations, the Soviet Union charges much lower prices for crude oil sold to the Free World than it charges to its satellite countries. For example, in 1962, the price of USSR

[17]National Petroleum Council, *Impact of Oil Exports from the Soviet Bloc*, Supplement to the 1962 Report, 1964, p. 18.
[18]*Ibid.*, p. 29.

20

crude oil exported to the Free World was $1.36/bbl. compared to $2.52/bbl. for crude oil sold to satellite countries, including Cuba.[19] It is obvious that making a profit on its crude oil operations is not a primary objective when sales to Free World countries are made at $1.36/bbl. Former Premier Khrushchev provided the key to their oil operations when he said, "We value trade least for economic reasons and most for political purposes."[20]

It appears likely that the Soviet Union will be able to continue to increase its crude oil producing capacity. It is estimated that in Russia there are 2.56 million square miles that are considered favorable for deposits of petroleum. This is somewhat more than the total area deemed to be favorable for petroleum deposits in the United States. The National Petroleum Council has concluded that the petroleum production levels in the USSR will not be limited by geologic factors for many years. For several years Russia has had more geophysical crews in operation than the entire Free World. The comprehensive pipe line system now under development to facilitate crude exports indicates that Russia intends to press forward with its crude oil export program.

The Communists consider the private oil industry to be a major symbol of the free enterprise system—a system which constitutes an obstacle to the spread of their own ideology and influence. Their objectives with respect to the Free World oil industry are reflected in an article in an authoritative Soviet publication which stated:

> It should be borne in mind that oil concessions represent, as it were, the foundation of the entire edifice of Western political influence in the (less developed) world, of all military bases and aggressive Blocs. If this foundation cracks, the entire edifice may begin to totter and then come tumbling down.[21]

[19]*Ibid.*, p. 7.
[20]*Ibid.*, p. 35.
[21]*Ibid.*, p. 42.

The National Petroleum Council has pointed out that the Communists are not simply trying to sell oil but to undermine and destroy the position of the private oil industry. The Soviet Union is using every means to encourage state control over oil in Free World countries and to incite the leaders of developing nations against the private oil industry. For our government to discourage the successful operation of its private oil industry in foreign countries through increased tax burdens or any other means would contribute substantially toward Russian success in its goals.

It is perfectly clear that American interests in foreign oil and gas production are important in U. S. efforts to compete with Russia in the Cold War. It must be recognized, however, that the industrial productivity of the U. S. is our basic strength. Since this industrial productivity is largely dependent on oil and gas for energy, an adequate domestic supply of petroleum is even more important to the U. S. than foreign supplies. Without a strong domestic economy and vigorous domestic industries, it would not be possible to be secure from a military standpoint or to be effective in the Cold War. It is essential, therefore, that our government encourage rather than discourage the efforts and expenditures that must be made on a continuing basis to provide an adequate domestic supply of energy.

# 4

# Risks in this Extractive Industry

If the importance of petroleum to the economy and the national security were the only basis for percentage depletion, the decision on continuance of the present rate would rest on the judgment of Congress whether there is any better way of accomplishing the beneficial results that flow from encouraging the development of adequate supplies of oil and gas. Another basic reason exists, however, for differential tax treatment of petroleum production. This reason is the unique nature of the exploration and development process for petroleum resources, and the high degree of risk inherent in these activities.

## Nature of the Petroleum Industry

Petroleum production is a mining venture with many characteristics of mining ventures in general and with some peculiarities of its own. Production inevitably depletes a wasting asset that occurs in natural form and that cannot be planted, grown and harvested; nor can it be manufactured. The search for most mineral deposits, particularly oil and gas, is characterized by great uncertainty. Even on successful ventures, there is a long time lag between outlay of funds and realization of earnings. Mineral production is also subject to the principle of diminishing returns and increasing costs. All of these circumstances justify differential treatment insofar as taxes on income are concerned in order to enable the mining industry to compete effectively with other industries in attracting capital.

Modern science has been challenged to devise ingenious methods to aid the prospector in his search for nature's most likely hiding places—structural traps, faults, folds, buried reefs, and other irregularities in the sedimentary rocks buried deep under the earth's crust. Even though geophysical tools such as the gravity meter, magnetometer, and seismograph have been useful in locating such possible hiding places, there is no assurance that there will be an accumulation of oil and gas. Only by drilling exploratory wells to test such traps, if they exist, can the prospector determine whether they actually contain commercial deposits of oil and gas. More often than not, years of collecting and interpreting data on a given prospective area end with a simple report: "The geology was perfect, the expected structure was found, but there was no oil or gas in it."

In 1959, the oil industry in the United States observed its 100th anniversary. It has come a long way from the completion of Col. Drake's 69½ foot well at Oil Creek, Pennsylvania, in August, 1859, to the completion in January, 1959, of a well in Pecos County, Texas, at a record depth of 25,-340 feet. Col. Drake's well produced 15 to 20 barrels a day. Despite a century of technological progress, the Pecos County well was a dry hole. This was not altogether unexpected, as many dry holes are drilled in the search for new deposits of oil and gas, and the trend is toward deeper and deeper drilling in less and less readily accessible areas. But the search must go on if our energy-sustained economy is to have an adequate supply of petroleum.

Col. Drake did not have the benefit of today's geological techniques, nor for that matter did he have particular need of such aids. Long before his time Indians had found oil escaping from seepages and floating on the surface of streams in northwestern Pennsylvania. Not only were oil and gas deposits in the vicinity of Oil Creek relatively easy to find from surface indications, but they could be reached with extremely shallow wells.

From such simple beginnings, the industry has progressed through ever-increasing complexities of exploration and development. Surface indications of underground deposits were the first to be tested by the prospector. These were the easiest to find. Then with expanding application of geological science, areas devoid of surface indications were explored and tested. Thus, many of the more likely prospects have been drilled.

The technical difficulties in locating oil deposits that may be several miles below the surface are characteristic of this unique business. But they are by no means the only features that distinguish it from other major non-extractive industries. For example, there is the peculiarity so aptly described by the statement, "When you find oil, you start going out of business." Except where withdrawals exceed the capacity of the natural replacement cycle, the supply of water in a water well is constantly being renewed by rainfall. The well at Cana mentioned in the New Testament is still a dependable source of water supply. But it never rains oil and oil reservoirs are never replenished.

The production of petroleum is a complex process that requires a thorough scientific knowledge of the characteristics of oil and gas reservoirs and their performance. Contrary to popular belief, oil is not found in underground lakes or streams but in tiny pores of rocks. A great variety of problems is involved in extracting the oil from these rock pores efficiently and economically.

Maximum recovery requires conservation of the natural gas and water pressures that are essential to move the oil out of the rock pores into the well pipe. Such conservation dictates a relatively slow rate of production, which defers producers' recovery of capital and realization of income.

## Discovery Record

Obviously, then, petroleum production differs sharply from non-extractive industries, both in the process of establishing productive capacity and in the existence of most of a producer's capital in the form of underground reserves. It also should be borne in mind that the discovery and development of these reserves, by their very nature, involve unusual risks.

Of the wells drilled in the search for new fields, only 1 in 9 finds any production, and only 1 in 46 finds deposits of 1,000,000 barrels or more of crude oil or an equivalent amount of energy in the form of natural gas (see Table 3).[22] As a general rule, a field of less than 1,000,000 barrels of oil or 6,000,000 mcf of gas is considered to be economically unprofitable.

Even after the discovery of oil or gas, a substantial number of wells drilled in the process of developing a field are dry holes, because of the difficulties of defining the limits of the productive area. Thus, since 1950, the percentage of *dry holes* drilled in developing known fields has ranged between 23 and 28 per cent and is now about 27 per cent.[23]

The preceding evidence shows that there is little similarity between the investment process required to establish petroleum production and that which is characteristic of other businesses. For a given cost, the manufacturer can build a plant of predictable size and capacity. With sound knowledge and planning he can create plants whose economic value bears a reasonably close relationship to expendi-

[22]*Bulletin of the American Association of Petroleum Geologists*, June, 1967, p. 984.
[23]*Oil and Gas Journal*, Annual Review and Forecast Issues, 1950-1967.

## TABLE 3
## NUMBER OF WELLS DRILLED FOR EACH DISCOVERY OF A FIELD WITH GIVEN ULTIMATE RECOVERY OF OIL OR GAS
### 1951-1960*

| Year | 1,000,000 barrels or more | 10,000,000 barrels or more | 50,000,000 barrels or more |
|------|---------------------------|----------------------------|----------------------------|
| 1951 | 40 | 155 | 549 |
| 1952 | 42 | 165 | 537 |
| 1953 | 40 | 184 | 1,658 |
| 1954 | 42 | 207 | 1,172 |
| 1955 | 47 | 215 | 1,936 |
| 1956 | 53 | 562 | 4,218 |
| 1957 | 44 | 199 | 756 |
| 1958 | 38 | 170 | 1,103 |
| 1959 | 58 | 391 | 1,758 |
| 1960 | 59 | 282 | 1,046 |
| Average | 46 | 221 | 1,074 |
| High | 59 | 562 | 4,218 |
| Low | 38 | 155 | 537 |

*The table refers only to the 17-state area which consists of Alabama, Arkansas, California, Colorado, Illinois, Indiana, Kansas, Kentucky, Louisiana, Michigan, Mississippi, Montana, Nebraska, New Mexico, Oklahoma, Texas, and Wyoming.

Source: Calculated from data published in *Bulletin of the American Association of Petroleum Geologists*, "North American Drilling Activity in 1966", by E. L. Dillon and L. H. Van Dyke, June, 1967. (One barrel of oil=6 mcf of gas.)

tures. Not so in the petroleum industry. In petroleum exploration, the prospector has little or no way of predicting what values he may realize or what his costs will be. In fact, he stands a good chance of losing his investment altogether. He can be certain that over the years he will lose money on unsuccessful ventures. His successful ventures, therefore, must yield profits that are great enough to cover all such losses.

Under these circumstances, it is not possible for each prospector to weigh anticipated costs against expected value and to make expenditures only when value will equal or exceed costs. For individual operators there is no necessary or predictable relationship between expenditures and values acquired.

This high degree of uncertainty is clearly illustrated in Table 3. In the years 1951-1960, the ratios of wildcatting success range from one in 38 to one in 59 for fields with reserves of 1 million barrels or more, and from one in 537 to one in 4,218 for the most productive new fields. These figures represent annual averages for the entire industry, including about 12,000 firms and individuals. Even wider fluctuations and greater uncertainty may be observed in most individual enterprises.

## Capital Requirements

Statistics compiled by the Chase Manhattan Bank indicate that expenditures by the petroleum industry for domestic exploration and development have amounted to about $45 billion during the ten-year period, 1957 through 1966.[24] During this ten-year period, proven reserves of liquid petroleum increased from 36 billion barrels to 39.8 billion barrels. Liquid petroleum reserves were equal to about 12 times annual production throughout this period. The fact that this ratio of reserves to production has been fairly stable over a long period of years indicates that expenditures in the past have been adequate to meet our petroleum needs. But what about the future? The U. S. Department of the Interior estimates that, if petroleum continues to supply about three-fourths of our energy needs, domestic consumption of oil will increase from 12.3 million barrels a day in 1967 to 17.6 million barrels a day in 1980.

On the basis of these estimates and the assumption that 78.5 percent of domestic demand will continue to be supplied by domestic production, U. S. production in the thirteen-year period, 1968-1980, will be over 55 billion barrels

---

[24]The Chase Manhattan Bank, *Capital Investments of the World Petroleum Industry*, 1966, pp. 24-25.

of liquid petroleum. In order to achieve this goal, the industry must find 75 billion barrels of new reserves during the same period. This will require substantial increases in amounts of capital dedicated to exploration and development efforts.

During the ten years, 1957-1966, exploration and development expenditures amounted to $1.46 per barrel of oil produced. If expenditures continue at the average rate of $1.46 per barrel produced, the amount of such expenditures during the thirteen years, 1968-1980, will be $80 billion. This would be an average of $6.2 billion a year, which is 40 percent more than the average annual expenditures in the ten-year period, 1957-1966. (See Figure 4).

There are some indications that oil and gas are becoming more difficult and costly to find. This means that amounts

## FIGURE 4
### ANNUAL EXPLORATION AND DEVELOPMENT EXPENDITURES REQUIRED TO SUPPLY U.S. OIL AND GAS NEEDS IN 1980

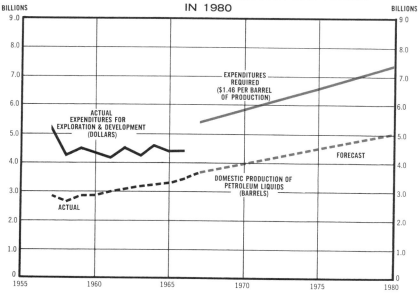

spent in search for new supplies may need to be even greater.

As we have shown, petroleum exploration is subject to many uncertainties apart from inherent technical problems. It is an endeavor that demands very large expenditures. From 3 to 10 years are needed to develop a potentially successful prospect into a profitable oil field. For all these reasons confidence in stability of the tax treatment of natural resources is of particular importance to the petroleum producer.

So long as there is assurance that the tax rules will not be changed, producers will continue to risk the large sums necessary to provide increasing supplies of oil and gas for the needs of our growing economy. But if confidence in stability of tax laws is seriously shaken, there is every reason to anticipate that expenditures will decrease, with the risk that future supplies will be less than we need for economic progress. The greatest contribution we can make toward preserving that confidence is to maintain adequate recognition of the unique character of the industry and the need for the effective incentive provided by percentage depletion.

# 5

# THE RECOVERY OF CAPITAL VALUE

The measurement of the capital component in the income stream is a comparatively simple problem in manufacturing and service enterprises where cost and value for individual projects are usually not substantially different. In extractive industries, however, and more particularly in the oil and gas industry, such measurement is difficult. The peculiarities of exploration and drilling for oil and gas mean that cost and value vary widely for individual ventures. Thus, conventional accounting concepts are inadequate measures of capital recoveries. The recovery of only the cost of a successful property cannot assure the accumulation of funds needed to replace that property when it becomes fully depleted. Reinvestment of capital recoveries alone will not preserve the income-producing capability of oil and gas operators. Just to stay in business, many oil producers must reinvest all of their capital recoveries plus a substantial part of their net income in the continuing search for new supplies.

## Early Depletion Legislation

From the inception of the United States income tax law on March 1, 1913, up to the beginning of World War I, income tax rates did not exceed 2 per cent on corporations or 7 per cent on individuals in the highest bracket. Technical precision in the measurement of capital recovery was not important because the tax drain on income did not interfere with the investment process. Depletion was based on the cost of individual properties acquired after March 1, 1913. But, for properties discovered before that date, the value as of March 1, 1913, was the basis for computing depletion. In most such cases, value was substantially higher than cost, a characteristic already noted. The revaluation of assets as of March 1, 1913, was not confined to extractive properties; it applied to any type of asset in the hands of any United States taxpayer in any line of business. However, the disparity between cost and value was of particular significance in extractive enterprises.

When we entered World War I in 1917, Congress enacted sharply increased income tax rates for both corporations and individuals. Rates on corporations reached a high of 80 per cent, while rates on individuals rose to a level of 77 per cent in the highest income bracket. The matter of capital recoveries immediately assumed critical importance if a business was to survive. This was especially true of oil and gas production, in which gross operating income is a complex mixture of capital recoveries and ordinary income. Had Congress perpetuated the use of historical cost as the basis for depletion on new mineral properties acquired after March 1, 1913, the finding effort might well have been seriously curtailed and the financial health of strategically important extractive industries impaired.

## The Discovery Value Principle

Congress recognized the situation in 1918 when it provided that depletion be based on the fair market value of the underground deposit on the date of discovery or within 30 days thereafter. This provision was referred to as "discovery value depletion" and was extended to cover newly discovered oil wells, gas wells, and mines. Thus, for income tax purposes, the computation of depletion deductions by a discoverer of a mineral property was placed on a basis comparable to that for a purchaser of a producing property.

Senator Penrose of Pennsylvania, a ranking member of the Senate Finance Committee, explained the new depletion provisions in a speech on the Senate floor. He said in part:

> The Committee gave very careful consideration to the question of depletion. The just taxation of incomes derived from the operation of mines and of oil and gas wells is a particularly difficult matter. This is due to the fact that part of what apparently is income is in reality a mere return of the capital of the enterprise. When, for example, a ton of coal is sold the excess of what is received from the cost of mining of that ton of coal is by no means all income; part of that excess must be treated as a repayment of what was invested in the mine from which the coal was taken. Such allowances for the extractive industries are covered by the depletion provisions. The Committee changed the language of this provision to assure continuance of the recognition of valuation of deposits as of March 1, 1913, as the basis for the deduction in the case of all property acquired by the taxpayer on or before that date. In pursuance of a policy permitting, so far as practicable, the development of new resources of this character they also provide for a more liberal allowance than was heretofore permitted in the case of newly discovered mines, or oil or gas wells, permitting the deduction to be based on the fair market value of property discovered instead of its cost.[25]

## Adoption of Percentage Depletion

Discovery value depletion proved difficult to administer because of controversies between taxpayers and the government on values of new discoveries. In 1926, at the request of the Treasury Department, Congress adopted percentage depletion in an effort to solve the administrative problems and, at the same time, provide results that would approxi-

[25]57 Congressional Record 549, 65th Congress, 3rd Session.

mate those under the discovery value rule. Consequently, the discovery value principle of depletion still stands today although the method of computing the deduction has been simplified. Since 1925, the deduction has been computed at 27½ per cent of gross income, but limited to 50 per cent of the net income from the property.

As a matter of fact, percentage depletion provides a deduction somewhat less than the current value of oil in the ground, as indicated by the actual prices currently being paid for proved reserves. According to a report on the financing of a number of property acquisitions involving over $1 billion financed by The Chase Manhattan Bank, some proved oil reserves in the ground to be produced in future years sold for as much as $1.35, and the average price paid was 93 cents per barrel.[26] This price of 93 cents represents more than 32 per cent of the average selling price of produced crude oil ($2.88 a barrel). Since 27½ per cent of the selling price is the maximum percentage depletion deduction, it is clear that percentage depletion provides an inadequate measure of the capital value of oil in the ground.

## The Capital Gain Alternative

The fact that the going price per barrel realized on sales of proved reserves is higher than percentage depletion per barrel undoubtedly weighs heavily in the decision of many operators to sell their producing properties outright. With respect to those properties sold which have been held for more than six months, the operator is entitled to compute his tax at the lower capital gains rates. In such situations an individual operator includes only 50 per cent of the net gain in his taxable income, and the resulting tax is limited to

[26]Bob T. H. Hulsey, *The Philosophy Behind Trading Oil Properties*, a paper presented at Economics and Valuation Symposium sponsored by Society of Petroleum Engineers, March 15-16, 1962.

25 per cent of the entire net gain. For corporations the capital gains tax is computed at a flat 25 per cent rate.

When an operator chooses to sell for a capital gain, he is foregoing continued operations of his properties—even with percentage depletion—in favor of present realization on his investment. That alternative would undoubtedly become much more attractive to many operators were the rate of percentage depletion reduced. Such sales of producing properties are undesirable to the extent that they absorb capital that would otherwise be spent in the search for new supplies. They also tend to reduce the number of operators engaged in exploration and drilling. Thus, sales of producing properties may contribute nothing toward finding new supplies of petroleum needed by our growing economy.

# 6

# PRICES, PROFITS AND TAXES

As a result of the incentive provided by percentage depletion, reserves have been discovered and developed more
rapidly than would otherwise have been the case. With more
production available, prices have tended to be lower. Thus,
because of percentage depletion, consumers have had more
petroleum products available at lower prices. At the same
time, profits of oil companies have been no more than reasonable, so that an increase in the total tax burden of the oil
industry could not be absorbed without a substantial effect
on either new investment or prices or both.

## Prices of Petroleum Products

The prices of petroleum products are generally lower in
the United States than in other industrial areas of the world.
The discovery of ample reserves of crude petroleum, technical progress in refining, and the development of markets
for other petroleum products enabled the petroleum industry to supply over 6.7 times as much gasoline in 1966 as
in 1926, the year percentage depletion for petroleum was
adopted by Congress. In addition, the product has been
made available at prices lower than in 1926, when retail
gasoline prices in 50 cities in the United States averaged 21
cents per gallon, exclusive of excise taxes. The comparable
average price (in the same cities) in 1966 for a product of
greatly superior quality was 20.5 cents per gallon (or about
half the retail price of a gallon of distilled water).[27] As

[27]American Petroleum Institute, *Highway Statistical and Financial Data*, July-
August, 1966.

# FIGURE 5

## THE REAL PRICE* OF GASOLINE

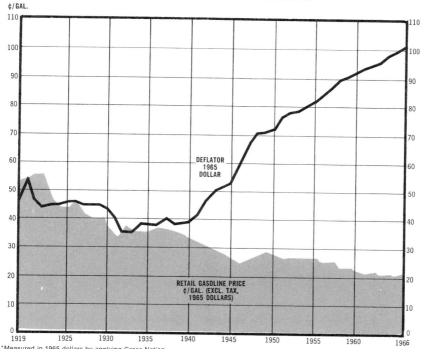

¢/GAL.

*Measured in 1965 dollars by applying Gross Nation-
al Product Implicit Price Deflators Calculated from
*Economic Report of the President*, January 1967.

Source: Retail price from American Petroleum Institute.

shown in Figure 5, gasoline prices in 1966, measured in constant value dollars, were lower than they were in 1926 when
percentage depletion provisions were first enacted. In constant 1966 dollars, the 1966 price of 20.5 cents per gallon
would be comparable to a 1926 price of 42.1 cents per gallon. And gasoline is a bargain compared with other commodities as reflected in the all-commodities price index as
shown in Figure 6.

The comparison of the current price of gasoline with the
price in 1926 does not tell the whole story, for the gasoline
of today is far superior. To measure the progress in both
engine and gasoline development, a realistic yardstick is

## FIGURE 6
### GASOLINE—A GREATER BARGAIN THAN EVER

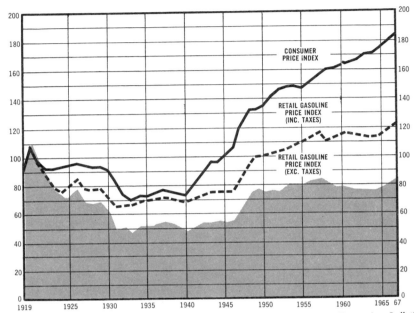

Source: Price Index: Bureau of Labor Statistics. Gasoline Prices: Tax Economics Bulletin of API.

needed, such as "ton-miles per gallon" (the number of miles that one gallon of gasoline can move one ton of automobile). Back in 1930, one gallon of gasoline could move one ton of the average automobile then in use a distance of 25 miles at 40 mph. By 1960, one gallon of gasoline could move one ton of the average automobile about 44 miles at the same speed.[28] That is a 75 per cent improvement. Of course, this improvement is not solely attributable to improved gasoline quality. Such progress is derived from technological advances in both the automotive and petroleum industries. The benefits of such progress are directly shared by every American.

During the period of over forty years since percentage

[28]Supplied by the Ethyl Corporation.

FIGURE 7

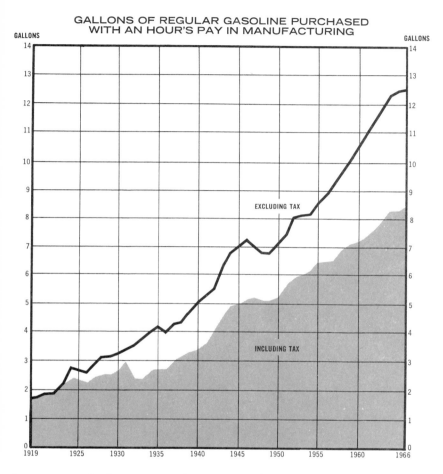

GALLONS OF REGULAR GASOLINE PURCHASED
WITH AN HOUR'S PAY IN MANUFACTURING

Source: Bureau of Labor Statistics and American Petroleum Institute

depletion was first enacted—a period during which the price of most items from newspapers to automobiles, from cigarettes to houses, has doubled or trebled—the price of gasoline has remained fairly stable. Today, with his higher wage, the average worker can buy over four times as much gasoline (of a far better quality) with one hour's earnings as he could buy in 1919. In fact, the pay for an hour's work buys more gasoline now than in any prior year. (See Figure 7.)

Without percentage depletion, gasoline prices would certainly have been considerably higher in the past. If depletion rates are reduced, future prices surely will be higher.

## Profits of the Oil Industry

Those who propose reductions in percentage depletion usually describe the oil industry as fabulously profitable and wealthy. This concept of the oil industry seems to be generally accepted by the public. The average citizen visualizes a single oil well as the key to great riches. Such concepts, of course, reflect a basic misunderstanding of the oil industry and an inadequate grasp of the facts about its operations and economics.

The average oil well in the United States produced only 14.2 barrels a day in 1966.[29] At a price of $2.88 a barrel, the operator of an average well would realize a gross income of about $36 a day after paying the royalty owner one-eighth of the value of production. This is less than the daily wage for a carpenter, plumber, bricklayer, or electrician. Moreover, from the $36 a day, the oil producer must recover the cost of drilling the well and must pay the operating expenses and ad valorem and production taxes.

The average well being drilled in the United States will produce only about 140,000 barrels of oil in its entire life. At the 14.2 barrels a day average rate of production, almost 30 years are required to recover 140,000 barrels. Thus, the average well is far from being the bonanza it is often thought to be.

Over the years, of course, there have been individuals who have been exceptionally successful in finding oil. As a

[29]United States Department of the Interior, Bureau of Mines, *Crude Petroleum and Petroleum Products*, August 24, 1967, p. 23.

result, they became wealthy, but there is nothing reprehensible about such success. As a matter of fact, these successful individuals took the risks that the percentage depletion provisions encouraged them to take and the results have contributed to the wealth and strength of the nation as a whole.

The corporations that constitute the major part of the oil industry have made substantial profits. Their profits, however, cannot be considered excessive by any reasonable standard. The fundamental measure of the earning capacity of an enterprise is the relationship of earnings to capital invested. Applying this measure, it is found that profits of oil companies are about the same as the average of all manufacturing industries.

A study made by The Chase Manhattan Bank of 29 of the largest U. S. oil companies showed that 1966 earnings averaged 12.1 per cent of invested capital. According to data compiled by The First National City Bank of New York, a larger group of oil companies averaged 12.6 per cent in 1966, compared to 14.1 per cent for all manufacturing companies. Over a twenty year period, 1947-1966, the average rate of return was 12.5 per cent for the oil companies, which compares to 12.7 per cent for all manufacturing companies (see Figure 8).

The June, 1967, issue of *Fortune* magazine published financial data on the 500 largest industrial companies in the United States. These data show that, of the 25 largest companies (determined on the basis of sales), seven were oil companies. From a profitability standpoint, however, the record is different. None of these seven oil companies that rank in the top 25 on the basis of sales were even in the top 100 when ranked on the basis of return on investment. The 500 companies in the *Fortune* study included 28 oil companies whose weighted average rate of return on investment was 12.3 per cent, compared to 13.6 per cent for the other companies.

# FIGURE 8

## RATE OF RETURN ON BOOK NET ASSETS
### 1947-1966

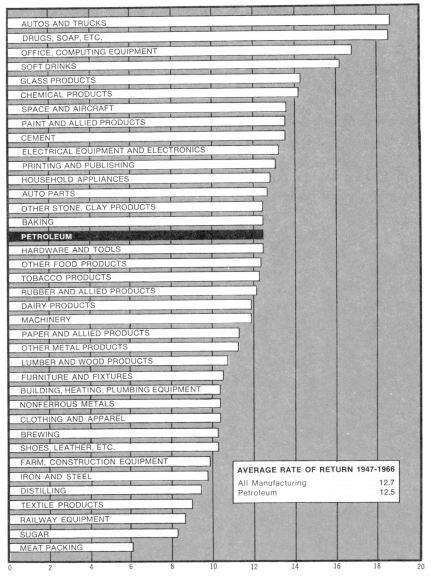

Source: Computed from The First National City Bank of New York data.

# Oil Industry's Tax Burden

In any discussion of the equity of a taxing system, no conclusion should be reached on the basis of a single type of tax. There may be differentials in the application of a particular tax, but no policy decision should be made until the effect of the whole range of tax burdens on that industry has been studied.[30] Such a study is beyond the scope of this booklet. However, it is significant that the opponents of percentage depletion who press for "neutrality" in income taxation frequently overlook the non-neutral effect of severance taxes on crude petroleum and of excise taxes on petroleum products. Obviously, all taxes imposed on an industry and its products must ultimately be reflected in prices if the industry is to continue to survive. Any tax is a burden on the industry to which it pertains because it affects product prices and profitability and tends to reduce the volume that can be sold. In the last ten years there have been substantial excise tax rate increases imposed on petroleum products by federal, state, and local governments. It has been the general experience that the oil industry has been forced to absorb a part of these increases because current competitive conditions made it impossible to pass on to consumers all of the additional taxes.

Petroleum Industry Research Foundation, Inc. made a recent study of the tax burden of the domestic oil industry as compared with that of other industries for the years 1964 and 1965, the latest years for which comparative data were

---

[30]This point has been made repeatedly by tax scholars. For example, see Richard Goode, *Corporation Income Tax*, John Wiley & Sons, New York, 1951, p. 145:
"One recurring theme of this study is that the corporation income tax cannot be appraised in isolation or in absolute terms."
Also, Louis Schreiber, *Consumption Taxes & Tax Reform*, National Industrial Conference Board Studies in Business Economics, No. 41, New York, 1953, p. 34:
"It is also clear to me that no single type of tax can be adequately appraised by itself. . . . Any tax must be examined as part of an entire tax structure of which it is, or is intended to be, a part."

available.[31] This report shows that the oil industry paid $2 billion in total domestic taxes in 1965, exclusive of motor fuel and other excise taxes of $7.6 billion. While the burden of federal income tax payments by the petroleum industry was a smaller percentage of gross revenues than for most other domestic industries, the incidence of other taxes (exclusive of motor fuel and excise taxes) was significantly higher for the oil industry than that for other industries generally.

The total taxes paid by the domestic petroleum industry for 1964 and 1965, exclusive of motor fuel and other excise taxes, averaged approximately 5.1 per cent of its gross domestic revenues for those years. The percentage was 5.4 per cent for all other mining and manufacturing industries for the same period. An earlier study by Petroleum Industry Research Foundation, Inc. for the years 1962 and 1963 disclosed comparable results.[32] For 1966, total taxes paid by the domestic petroleum industry (exclusive of $8 billion of motor fuel and other excise taxes) was approximately $2.5 billion, which was over 6 per cent of gross domestic revenues. Information for all mining and manufacturing corporations for 1966 is not yet available, but the indications are that their tax burden was not significantly higher than in 1965. The oil industry's tax payments of $2 billion in 1965 were equal to approximately 18 per cent of the total value added by the industry, an increase from 15.7 per cent in 1963. By comparison, the total domestic taxes imposed on all mining and manufacturing industries in 1963, the latest year for which information is available, were equal to only about 12 per cent of the total value added by those industries.[33]

If motor fuel and other excise taxes are included, the oil industry's total tax burden was over 21 cents per dollar of

[31]Petroleum Industry Research Foundation, Inc., *The Tax Burden on the Domestic Oil and Gas Industry*, 1964-1966, March, 1968.
[32]Petroleum Industry Research Foundation, Inc., *The Tax Burden on the Domestic Oil and Gas Industry*, 1962-1963, October, 1965, p. 5.
[33]Ibid., p. 12.

revenue for 1966, which is about four times as great as that of other industries. According to this study, total oil industry domestic tax payments for 1966, including motor fuel and excise taxes, amounted to about $10.5 billion. This was equal to approximately $3 per barrel of domestic crude oil and natural gas liquids produced in 1966.

These studies clearly indicate that the oil industry is paying a fair share of total taxes. In any event, however, it is most unlikely that total tax revenues could be increased by reducing percentage depletion. Any reduction in depletion would probably result in a reduction of expenditures for finding and developing new oil and gas reserves, which would have a detrimental effect on the entire economy of the nation. The following side effects might also be expected:

1. Reductions in drilling would reduce the market for steel, curtail the revenues of a large number of companies providing a wide variety of services to oil companies, and create greater unemployment in the oil business and related industries.

2. With increasing scarcity of petroleum, prices would probably rise, over a period of years, increasing tax deductions of businesses consuming petroleum and increasing costs to the federal government which purchased in 1967 over 360 million barrels of petroleum (a tenth of our total domestic consumption) for military use alone.[34]

3. Greater scarcity and increased prices would tend to reduce petroleum consumed which would have a significant impact on excise tax revenues of each state as well as the federal government.

4. The rate of return on investments of oil companies (presently no higher than other industries) would be reduced.

[34]Source: Department of Defense, Defense Fuel Supply Center.

# 7

# FOREIGN PRODUCTION
# AND PERCENTAGE DEPLETION

The taxation of American-owned firms operating abroad is a technical subject involving the interrelation of many domestic laws and regulations as well as many tax treaties. There is no mystery about the manner in which the United States taxes its firms operating abroad, but the complexities invite misunderstanding. Accordingly, before turning to the role of foreign depletion in U. S. tax calculations, it may be helpful to review briefly the general background of the subject.

## Taxation of Income from Foreign Production
When the United States shaped its first general income tax laws in the years following 1913, the pattern was established of applying the tax uniformly to all United States citizens and taxpayers on a worldwide basis—irrespective of geographical considerations. Since the United States had established a pattern of uniform application of income tax worldwide, it was certainly not an accident that discovery value depletion and its successor, percentage depletion, were applicable to petroleum production wherever located.

Foreign countries assert first right to tax the profits derived from within their countries just as our government asserts the right to tax income from within the U. S. This concept is applicable for all businesses within the foreign borders and not just for petroleum operations. Obviously, a U. S. company could not pay both foreign tax and the U. S. tax and remain competitive since its foreign competitors do not bear such a double burden. In fact, many of these foreign competitors are agencies of their governments and are not subject to any income tax. Still others are corporations domiciled in countries that impose no income tax on their income from foreign sources. Consequently, almost since their inception, the U. S. tax laws have permitted the U. S. taxpayer to credit against his U. S. income tax the foreign income taxes paid. But the credit is so limited that the total taxes paid are equal to the higher of the U. S. tax or the foreign tax but not both. Thus, whether engaged in cotton trading, electrical equipment manufacturing, or oil production, a U. S. taxpayer's foreign operations have no income tax advantage over domestic operations. This conclusion was confirmed by a special committee of the Independent Petroleum Association of America after a thorough study to determine whether the foreign operations of U. S. oil companies have any such tax advantage.[35]

In most foreign countries, the government owns the basic mineral rights. Consequently, companies producing oil and gas abroad must pay royalties to the host government. These royalty payments are made at rates equal to or greater than those prevailing in the U. S. In addition, the governments of the foreign countries levy income taxes just as our government levies an income tax on foreigners who produce oil and gas in the U. S. Only the income taxes paid to the foreign governments, however, qualify for the foreign tax

[35]In 1965, many independent oil producers were concerned about imports of foreign crude oil. Some felt that the low cost of foreign crude might be attributable in some way to tax advantages that were not available to domestic producers. A Special Committee on Foreign Taxation was appointed to study this question and, after a thorough study, reached the conclusion indicated above.

credit against the U. S. tax. Under no circumstances are the royalty payments treated as a part of the foreign tax credited against the U. S. tax liability.

## Effect on U. S. Tax Revenues of a Change in Foreign Depletion

Because income tax structures differ so widely around the world it is impossible to generalize concerning the effects of a change in the U. S. depletion provisions for foreign production. It is very unlikely, however, that any significant increase in U. S. tax revenue would result from reducing percentage depletion deductions on foreign production. Acknowledging this, Mr. Douglas Dillon, formerly Secretary of the Treasury, stated that the changes proposed in 1963 would not have any particular effect on U. S. taxation of oil produced abroad. He said further,

> Taxation of companies abroad is generally—of oil companies —is generally tied in so closely with the taxation of the country in which they operate, and countries have set their tax rates always either at the same level or slightly higher than the United States, that the net effect of any change we have there would merely mean that the companies would pay higher taxes to some foreign countries rather than the United States.[36]

Thus, in many cases, a reduction in the U. S. depletion provision would not result in any additional tax payments to the U. S. Treasury. Where such additional tax liabilities were created, foreign nations would be encouraged to increase their tax rates so as to capture any additional taxes. In any event, there would be little, if any, gain to the U. S. Treasury.

The foreign competitors of American firms operating abroad would not be directly affected by a change in the

[36]Hearings Before the Committee on Ways and Means, 88th Congress, First Session, on the Tax Recommendations of the President Contained in His Message Transmitted to Congress January 24, 1963, Part 1, p. 606.

U. S. depletion provision. Thus, to the extent that the tax payments by U. S. firms should be increased by such a change, their position would be weakened with respect to foreign competitors.

## Foreign Crude Oil and National Security

Encouragement of American companies to secure mineral rights in foreign countries is desirable from the standpoint of national security. The importance of access to foreign oil was graphically demonstrated in both world wars. Much of the oil used in World War I came from foreign sources. In World War II, about one billion barrels of foreign oil were used in the military operations of the United States and its allies. During the Suez Crisis of 1956 and the Arab-Israeli conflict of 1967, the availability of alternative foreign sources of supply averted a major energy shortage in Europe and may well have prevented the escalation of those crises into major armed conflicts. A broadly based source of supply thus not only simplifies the logistics of war, but may well prevent hostilities. For a more complete discussion of the national security aspects of depletion, references should be made to Section 3 of this booklet.

## Impact on U. S. Balance of Payments

Foreign operations of the American oil industry are making a positive contribution toward a favorable balance of payments. In a recent publication of the First National City Bank of New York, it was stated that,

> . . . oil transactions as a whole have been adding more— probably between $250 million and $500 million a year more —to the U. S. payments balance than they have been taking away from it.[37]

[37]Edward Symonds, *Oil in The National Balance*, First National City Bank, New York, June 28, 1965, p. 4.

To the extent that a reduction in depletion should result in some additional taxation by the U. S. or foreign governments, it would tend to aggravate the nation's balance of payments problem. Any relatively small increase in taxes which might result from such a change in depletion would not be sufficient to offset the basic cost advantage of foreign crude. Thus, a reduction in foreign depletion would not serve to reduce petroleum imports. Importers would continue to bring in the full quota although their outpayments might rise slightly as a result of possibly higher taxes.

In the highly competitive foreign markets, price differentials of only a few cents can significantly influence sales. Since U. S. firms operating abroad sell about 80 per cent of their foreign production in foreign markets, any increase in costs would impair their position with respect to foreign competitors. If this position is impaired, U. S. exports of non-petroleum products would be reduced as a consequence of any curtailment of overseas operations of U. S. petroleum companies. The position of U. S. firms with respect to Russia and its satellites would also be impaired. To the extent that the competitive position of U. S. firms is injured, their foreign sales and earnings would decline and the level of repatriated earnings would drop. Thus, any impact of a cut in foreign depletion on our nation's balance of payments could only be adverse.

## Aid to Friendly Nations

The U. S. has undertaken the responsibility of supplying aid to less developed countries in an effort to bring their economies up to the higher standards prevailing elsewhere. Billions of dollars have been spent in implementation of this program, and additional billions will be spent in the future. The burden of our foreign aid program on our national economy may be reduced, however, to the extent that the resources of the poorer countries can be developed.

The most pressing needs of the less developed nations are for schools, roads, hospitals and other facilities normally paid for through taxes in the United States. These less developed nations usually lack the resources to make the desired social investments, and thus rely heavily on foreign capital to provide the necessary investment. U. S.-owned oil companies operating abroad have invested large amounts of money directly in such facilities in oil producing areas of less developed countries and have thereby reduced the need for foreign aid.

Several less developed nations are also channeling tax and royalty revenues from oil operations into various development programs. An excellent example can be found in Saudi Arabia. In 1946 the Arab Industrial Development Department was set up in Saudi Arabia to help start new businesses. Funds for this program were provided by the Saudi Arabian government through revenue from oil operations. In addition, Kuwait and Libya are beginning to channel oil revenues effectively into new development projects and the recent discovery of oil in Nigeria is permitting that nation to take significant strides toward becoming a viable industrial nation. Oil revenues in Venezuela have been channeled into several major industrial projects and the Venezuelan economy is much sounder than that of most other Latin American republics. Through such development programs, the need for foreign aid payments has been reduced.

Any reduction in tax incentives for foreign production would tend to discourage the flow of investments in such less developed nations. This would be contrary to the objectives of the Alliance for Progress and to our government's current policy of encouraging investments in less developed countries.

# 8

# CONCLUSION

Petroleum supplies are more important to us today than ever before in our history. They are indispensable to our national security and our standard of living. Our continued economic progress depends primarily upon increased productivity that can come only from the use of more machines and energy. Liquid fuels derived from petroleum are of strategic importance in the struggle for world peace, progress, and prosperity. We must, therefore, make every effort to assure that they continue to be adequate in the future because we cannot afford to take unnecessary risks with our national security and economic progress.

An adequate supply of petroleum depends, however, on a fair rate of return to the petroleum industry, commensurate with the risks involved. As this booklet clearly demonstrates, substantial risks are inherent in the exploration for oil and gas. Nevertheless, the rate of return on capital invested in the petroleum industry is comparable to that for manufacturing generally. Thus, although the present percentage depletion provisions have encouraged the exploration for oil, they certainly have not generated unduly large profits for the oil producers. Rather, the consumers and the nation generally have benefited through the availability of oil in ample quantities and at reasonable prices.

The petroleum industry contributes significantly to the revenues of federal, state, and local governments. Even though percentage depletion has reduced the burden of the federal income tax on the petroleum industry, the heavy incidence of the various other taxes on the oil industry has offset this advantage even if motor fuel and other excise taxes are excluded. If these taxes are included, the oil industry's total tax burden was over 21 cents per dollar of revenue in 1966, which is about four times as great as that of most other industries.

Finally, the present percentage depletion rate has not resulted in the discovery of too much oil. In retrospect, it is doubtful if our nation could have achieved and retained her position of world leadership without the major contribution of the petroleum industry. Thus, we endorse the conclusions of the President's Materials Policy Commission, as stated in a report to the President of the United States, as follows:

> First, the device of percentage depletion is a powerful inducement to capital to enter the relatively risky business of searching for mineral deposits of uncertain location, quality, and extent. Where the national need is great, there is justification for using a higher percentage rate than might be appropriate if recovery of capital investment were the sole objective.
>
> \* \* \*
>
> In short, the device of percentage depletion as an incentive to mineral exploration is not without its limitations. But no alternative method of taxation has come to the Commission's attention or could be devised by the Commission which, in its judgment, promises to overcome these limitations and still achieve the desired results, particularly not without seriously dislocating well established capital values and other arrangements in the industries concerned, with highly adverse effects on supply. Taking the practical situation as it finds it, the Commission believes that any radical alteration of existing tax arrangements would be undesirable.[38]

[38]The President's Materials Policy Commission, *Resources for Freedom*, "Foundations for Growth and Security," Vol. 1, U. S. Government Printing Office, Washington, D. C., June, 1952, p. 35.

# ANALYSIS OF CRITICISMS AGAINST

# PERCENTAGE DEPLETION

# ANALYSIS OF CRITICISMS AGAINST PERCENTAGE DEPLETION

In spite of the unique characteristics of the oil industry and its contribution to our national welfare and security, and in spite of the importance of the depletion provisions to our national economy, there are critics who maintain that these provisions in our revenue laws are undesirable for one reason or another. Answers to most of the major criticisms lodged against percentage depletion may be found in the body of this booklet. However, because the answers to the criticisms are scattered throughout the text, this appendix has been added to provide the interested reader a brief statement of the more cogent points to consider when analyzing particular criticisms of percentage depletion. Careful consideration of these points, we believe, will demonstrate the desirability of retaining the current percentage depletion provisions.

## The Criticisms

|  | Page |
|---|---|
| Depletion and the Tax Rate | 57 |
| Distribution of Benefits | 58 |
| Percentage Depletion at Graduated Rates | 59 |
| Insurance Principle | 60 |
| Subsidization of Marketing | 61 |
| Conservation and Over-Consumption | 63 |
| Tax Neutrality | 64 |
| A Fair Share of Taxes | 66 |
| Depletion—A Tax Loophole | 67 |
| Foreign Depletion | 67 |
| Foreign Royalties and Income Taxes | 69 |
| Double Deduction | 70 |

# DEPLETION AND THE TAX RATE

## The Criticism:

When percentage depletion was first enacted in 1926, the income tax rate on corporations was only 13 per cent. Today, with a corporate tax rate of 48 per cent, depletion is providing greater benefits than Congress intended.

## Points to Consider:

1. When the income tax was first imposed in 1913, the tax rates were no more than 2 per cent for corporations. Technical precision in the measurement of capital recovery was not important because the tax drain did not interfere significantly with the investment process. When tax rates increased drastically during World War I, however, the discovery value principle was adopted for computing depletion deductions.

2. When Congress adopted the principle of depletion deductions in excess of cost—that is, when it established the discovery value provisions in 1918—the income and excess profits tax rates ran as high as 80 per cent. Percentage depletion was adopted in 1926 for the purpose of simplifying the mechanics of determining the deductions, but it was Congress' intent to allow about the same amount as under the "discovery value" provisions. As a matter of fact, percentage depletion deductions are now less per barrel than the average value of oil in the ground. This, together with the fact that tax rates are lower now than in 1918, would indicate that, if anything, percentage depletion is now providing smaller benefits than intended by Congress when the basic depletion provisions were adopted in 1918.

3. Because of the increase in corporate tax rates every tax deduction is "worth" nearly four times as much today as it was in 1926. It makes no more sense to propose a reduction in the depletion deduction than it does to propose a reduction in any other business deduction on the grounds that the tax benefit of today's deduction was never intended by Congress.

# DISTRIBUTION OF BENEFITS

## The Criticism:

The percentage depletion provisions benefit the big oil companies which produce most of the oil rather than the small companies which find most of it.

## Points to Consider:

1. The determination of the percentage depletion deduction does depend upon the production of oil rather than upon discovery of oil. However, since approximately 90 per cent of all the oil produced is produced by the operators who drill the wells that develop the reserves, the benefits of percentage depletion accrue in large measure to the companies finding the oil.

2. In numerous instances the small operator benefits from extensive geological and geophysical work conducted at great expense by the larger oil companies. In addition, the small operator often reduces his capital risked in a drilling venture by obtaining financial assistance of larger companies through "dry-hole" and/or "bottom-hole" contributions and by employing various sharing arrangements. Although there is little doubt that small operators drill a large number of the exploratory wells, there is a question as to whether they find a proportionately large share of the reserves. In any event, even though many discoveries may be credited to small operators, the larger companies provide the major part of the risk capital employed by the industry. The companies that provide the risk capital, generally, get title to oil discovered and, as a matter of equity, should have the right to claim the depletion deductions when the oil is produced.

3. Some small operators sell producing properties after they have been developed and this practice tends to increase the larger companies' volume of production, but the amounts involved are not of great significance in relation to total production. Even when the small operator sells out, however, he gets indirect benefits from percentage depletion because he is able to secure a better price for producing properties than would be possible without percentage depletion.

# PERCENTAGE DEPLETION AT GRADUATED RATES

## The Criticism:

The present percentage depletion provisions provide unduly large benefits to a few large oil companies. To correct this imbalance, percentage depletion should be allowed at graduated rates with the smaller firms receiving the higher depletion rates. (One such proposal suggests that the 27½ per cent rate be retained for taxpayers whose gross income from the production of oil and gas is less than $1,000,000; that a 21 per cent rate be allowed on such income between $1,000,000 and $5,000,000; and that a rate of 15 per cent be allowed on gross income in excess of $5,000,000.)

## Points to Consider:

1. This criticism stems in part from the common misconception that the petroleum industry is dominated by a few very large firms. The following statistics for 1963 show that a high degree of concentration is not typical of the petroleum industry.

| Industry | Measure of Concentration | Percent Accounted for by | |
|---|---|---|---|
| | | Top 4 Firms | Top 8 Firms |
| Cigarettes | Value of Shipments | 80 | 100 |
| Primary Copper | Value of Shipments | 78 | 98 |
| Automobiles and Parts | Value of Shipments | 79 | 83 |
| Aircraft Engines | Value of Shipments | 56 | 77 |
| Petroleum Refining | Value of Shipments | 34 | 56 |
| Petroleum Production | Net Crude Oil Production | 24 | 37 |

2. Decreased rates of depletion for the firms that make the more substantial contributions to the nation's supply of energy would discourage growth at precisely the time we need a growing industry.

3. The larger firms include hundreds of thousands of stockholders owning less than 100 shares each. In the end, it is the individual shareholders of the larger companies who would be penalized by graduated percentage depletion rates. The

smaller producers are either individuals with substantial resources or small corporations that are owned by one or a very few individuals; yet these firms would receive the greatest benefit from percentage depletion at graduated rates.

4. Many inequities in tax treatment would result from graduated percentage depletion rates. These inequities are best illustrated by jointly owned (or unitized) properties. In such cases each co-owner, regardless of size, owns a share of the same property; bears a proportionate share of all costs; and takes the same degree of risk as other co-owners holding equal interests in the property. To require one of these co-owners to use a rate of percentage depletion that is lower than that used by another co-owner would be clearly discriminatory and inequitable.

5. The purpose of percentage depletion is to provide an incentive to find and produce more oil. To reduce this incentive for the more effective operators would tend to remove or nullify the incentive for all operators.

# INSURANCE PRINCIPLE

## The Criticism:

Percentage depletion cannot be justified by the high risks of the oil industry because the risks can be minimized by application of the "insurance principle." This means that each of the larger companies can drill enough wells each year to be sure that the results approximate the national average.

## Points to Consider:

1. About one out of nine exploratory wells drilled in the United States is classed as "successful;" that is, it results in some commercial production. The fact that this figure has been relatively stable over a long period of time has led to the mistaken belief that industrial firms can accurately predict the outcome of their exploratory ventures and thus reduce their risks to a matter of cost accounting. The one in nine ratio relates solely to geological, not economic, factors; a geologic

"success" may well be a financial fiasco. Only one in 46 exploratory wells finds a commercially profitable field, on the average. This figure is not nearly as stable from year to year as the one in nine ratio and has shown substantial variability. In the ten years, 1951-1960, only one in 1,074 wildcats, on the average, resulted in finding one of the very large fields which generate a large part of the industry's earnings. This ratio has fluctuated from a high of one in 537 wells for such large fields in 1952 to a low of one in 4,218 in 1956. Clearly the variability of the results of exploratory drilling is so great as to eliminate any so-called "insurance principle." (See Table 3, p. 27.)

2. There is wide variation in exploratory well costs; some shallow wells cost only a few thousand dollars while some of the very deep holes cost more than a million dollars. Obviously, therefore, the financial risk varies tremendously from one well to the next and success ratios based on the number of wells alone fail to give an adequate measure of the financial risks.

3. Another factor which leads to confusion is that the one in nine ratio refers to an industry wide average over the entire United States; but the industry comprises some 12,000 business entities, the largest of which drills only about 3 per cent of the exploratory wells drilled in any year. Individual firms simply do not drill enough wells to be able to rely safely on the law of averages. In fact, the success ratios of the largest firms vary widely from year to year. Thus, despite substantial drilling efforts, some of the largest oil companies have failed to find enough new oil to replace reserves depleted by production — not only in a particular year, but over periods of many years.

# SUBSIDIZATION OF MARKETING

## The Criticism:

The vertically integrated companies utilize percentage depletion to subsidize marketing operations and to offset marketing losses with production profits.

# Points to Consider:

1. The gross outlays for exploration, development, and production operating expenses have consumed nearly all the gross revenues from U. S. production. Operators have plowed back a substantial portion of their profits and all the cash generated by depletion, depreciation, and amortization just to stay in business. Thus there simply is no appreciable surplus of funds available for subsidization of the marketing function in major companies.

2. Many non-integrated marketing companies have operated profitably over a period of years and have not only competed successfully with integrated companies, but have improved their marketing positions despite fluctuating prices and profit margins. If independent marketers can make profits, it is logical to conclude that the integrated companies have been able to make profits on their marketing operations and that there is no subsidization involved.

3. The conservation rules and the proration formulas of the principal producing states operate to restrict each producer to only his prorata share of production. Consequently, increases in volumes of products marketed by an integrated company do not result in a corresponding increase in his crude oil production. This fact indicates that an integrated company must justify new marketing investments on the basis of profits to be derived from the marketing function alone. Since most large companies are continually expanding their marketing facilities, it must be concluded that their marketing operations are profitable.

4. Vertical integration in every major industry is a common and natural method of diversification which provides insulation from wide profit fluctuations associated with specialization in a single phase of business activity. Consequently, vertical integration is a stabilizing factor in our economy which should be encouraged rather than discouraged. Equivalent economic stability probably could not be achieved even through extensive use of direct government controls over prices, outputs, and profits. For an excellent, detailed, and impartial study, reaching the same conclusion, see John G. McLean and Robert W. Haigh, *The Growth of Integrated Oil Companies*, Harvard Business School, 1954.

# CONSERVATION AND OVER-CONSUMPTION

## The Criticism:

Percentage depletion stimulates production, artifically lowers the price of petroleum production, and, therefore, operates to defeat conservation of petroleum resources by encouraging over-consumption.

## Points to Consider:

1. A high level of energy utilization is desirable in that it is the key to economic growth and prosperity. Energy consumption should thus be encouraged so long as it does not result in wasteful production practices.

2. A high level of consumption is also essential to a successful national petroleum policy because the most economical method of meeting a surge in military requirements is by diversion of civilian consumption. In fact, this may be the only effective source in a national emergency because the time lapse between first exploratory efforts and complete development of an oil field in the United States is usually at least three years and often ten years or more. Thus, unless a high level of private consumption is maintained, there will be no supply available to divert to military uses.

3. In spite of the phenomenal growth in demand for domestic petroleum during the last 40 years, the industry has been able to develop sufficient resources to meet the demand and has maintained reserves at a fairly constant level of 12 times annual production. (See page 12.) There is no indication that the industry will be unable to meet the demand for petroleum for many years to come. (See pages 12 to 14.)

4. The domestic industry has the capacity to produce almost 12 million barrels daily while following sound conservation practices. Actual production is about 4 million barrels daily less than productive capacity. It follows that high levels of consumption have not led to wasteful conservation practices.

5. Depletion provisions play a vital role in generating and attracting funds for the heavy expenditures required in such

conservation measures as water floods, pressure maintenance and repressuring projects, miscible-phase operations,
and the newly developed fire floods or thermal recovery programs. Without percentage depletion many such secondary recovery projects would never be undertaken, and billions of
barrels of oil would be lost to the economy.

# TAX NEUTRALITY

## The Criticism:

The differential tax treatment implicit in percentage depletion violates "tax neutrality" and results in a misallocation
of economic resources.

## Points to Consider:

1. This criticism presupposes that the federal income tax is
the only tax in existence. Certainly any measure of the neutrality of taxes on resource allocation must consider not only
the income tax, but also the sales, excise, property, severance,
and other taxes, whether imposed by the federal, state, or local government. The distribution among income taxes and
other taxes varies widely between the oil industry and American industry in general. But, the total tax burden of the U. S.
oil industry, excluding motor fuel and other excise taxes, is
equal to that of the average U. S. industrial corporation and
is considerably higher if such excise and sales taxes are included. For more comprehensive discussion of the taxes imposed on the oil and gas industry, see pages 43 to 45.

2. The national interest may dictate an "optimum" allocation
of resources in some pattern other than that which would result from solely free-market forces. The federal government
has for many years deliberately affected the resource allocation pattern by extending financial assistance in one form or
another to small business, the maritime industry, the non-
ferrous metal industry, agriculture, and many other businesses. Considering the importance of the oil and gas industry to economic progress and to national security, the economic incentives provided by percentage depletion are rea-

sonable and desirable. For a more complete discussion of the substantial contributions of the oil and gas industry to the United States, see pages 4 to 22.

3. The theory of tax neutrality, if accepted in principle and applied correctly, would require appropriate differentials for unusual conditions in order to avoid an inefficient allocation of capital. To illustrate, assume that there are two industries alike in all respects except that industry A, which is labor intensive, has one dollar of capital per dollar of annual sales whereas industry B, which is capital intensive, has three dollars of capital per dollar of annual sales. If the rate of return is 10 per cent in both industries, then for each dollar of sales there will be 10¢ of profit for industry A and 30¢ for industry B, as shown below:

|  | Industry A | Industry B |
|---|---|---|
| Capital Invested | $100 | $300 |
| Sales | $100 | $100 |
| Costs | 90 | 70 |
| Profit (10 Per Cent of Capital) | $ 10 | $ 30 |

If income taxes were imposed at a 50 per cent rate, prices would have to be adjusted so that both industries would continue to make the same return after taxes if they were to attract the necessary capital inputs. The income tax would force industry B to charge 30 per cent more per unit whereas A would need to charge only 10 per cent more, as indicated below:

|  | Industry A | Industry B |
|---|---|---|
| Capital Invested | $100 | $300 |
| Sales (adjusted to yield a net profit of 10 per cent of investment) | $110 | $130 |
| Costs | 90 | 70 |
| Profit, before Taxes | $ 20 | $ 60 |
| Income Tax at 50 Per Cent | 10 | 30 |
| Profit (10 Per Cent of Capital) | $ 10 | $ 30 |

These changes would alter the relative demands for the two products and would cause an inefficient diverson of capital from industry B to industry A. If 50 per cent of B's net income before taxes were exempted from tax, however, the

65

price of B's product would need to rise only 10 per cent to restore the pre-tax profit margins. In this case both prices would rise by 10 per cent and, since relative prices would be unchanged, the tax would be neutral. Thus, differences which may exist in the economy may require differential tax treatment if neutrality is to be achieved. The example is particularly pertinent since petroleum is much more capital intensive than manufacturing in general.

4. The theory of non-neutral taxation suffers from an additional flaw. Even if all industries were alike in respect to capital utilization and rate of return, it would not necessarily follow that a departure from equal tax treatment would lead to non-neutrality. If there were no tax differentials in such a hypothetical system, a single case of differential treatment could be regarded as non-neutral. In reality, however, the system is far from being "optimal" because of a multitude of differential provisions such as those relating to agriculture, small business, cooperatives, and others. Thus, it does not necessarily follow that an additional differential results in further non-neutrality. In fact, an additional differential is as likely to lead toward neutrality as toward non-neutrality.

# A FAIR SHARE OF TAXES

## The Criticism:

The oil and gas industry does not pay its "fair share" of taxes when compared with those of other industries.

## Points to Consider:

1. It is true that the impact of federal income taxes on earnings of oil companies is lighter than on most other industries because of percentage depletion and other tax provisions. But other taxes, excluding motor fuel and other excise taxes, fully offset the lower income tax burden. As a result, in 1964 and 1965, the taxes paid by the domestic petroleum industry,

exclusive of motor fuel and excise taxes, were more than 5 per cent of its gross domestic revenues. This percentage was essentially the same as that for all mining and manufacturing industries.

2. If motor fuel and other excise taxes are included, the oil industry's tax payments amounted to $10.5 billion in 1966, and represented over 21 per cent of gross revenues. This indicates that the oil industry's tax burden is about four times as great as that of most other industries. (See pp. 43-45.)

# DEPLETION - A TAX LOOPHOLE

## The Criticism:

Percentage depletion as applied to oil and gas production constitutes a "loophole" in our federal income tax system.

## Points to Consider:

1. A loophole is defined as an ambiguity or omission in the text through which the intent of a statute may be circumvented. The percentage depletion provisions have been clearly set out in the Internal Revenue Code since 1926.

2. They have been critically examined many times by Congress, and it is manifestly incorrect and unfair to brand them as a loophole. See the Legislative History in Appendix B of this booklet for a detailed account of the careful attention these provisions have received from Congress.

# FOREIGN DEPLETION

## The Criticism:

Percentage depletion on foreign production does not contribute to national security. Its elimination would (1) serve to generate more revenues for the U. S. Treasury, (2) make domestic production relatively more attractive, and (3) improve the nation's balance of payments.

## Points to Consider:

1. The taxation of the income of all U. S. citizens and taxpayers is applied uniformly regardless of geographical considerations. The foreign tax credit limits the total income taxes paid on any foreign source income to an amount equal to the higher of the U. S. tax or the foreign tax but not both. Thus, whether engaged in cotton trading, electrical equipment manufacturing, or crude oil production, a U. S. taxpayer's foreign operations have no tax advantage over domestic operations.

2. It is very unlikely that any significant increase in U. S. tax revenue would result from reducing percentage depletion on foreign production. Where additional U. S. tax liabilities were created, foreign governments would be encouraged to raise their tax rates to capture any additional taxes. Through the foreign tax credit, these higher foreign taxes could be offset against the higher U. S. tax liability and there would be no gain for the U. S. Treasury.

3. Foreign depletion encourages American firms to develop reserves in foreign areas. These reserves make a significant contribution to national security. Much of the oil used in World War I came from foreign sources, and the United States and its allies used over a billion barrels of foreign oil for military purposes in World War II. Widely dispersed sources of supply increase military flexibility and permit shorter supply lines.

4. Elimination or reduction of the tax incentives for foreign production would tend to increase the costs of U. S. operators in foreign areas but the increase would be far too small to offset the economic advantages of foreign crude. Consequently, domestic importers would continue to have a real incentive to import their full quotas. Even a small increase in costs, how-

ever, would impair the position of U. S. firms operating in the intensely competitive foreign areas. Any such impairment could reduce their profits, and as a result, repatriated earnings would decline.

5. Foreign operations of the American oil industry are making a positive contribution toward a favorable balance of payments. Elimination or reduction of tax incentives for foreign production would tend to widen the nation's balance of payments deficit (see pages 49 to 50), first, through higher prices for foreign crude oil imports and, second, through lower profits of American companies selling foreign oil abroad.

# FOREIGN ROYALTIES AND INCOME TAXES

## The Criticism:

U. S.-owned oil companies operating abroad obtain excessive foreign tax credits against their U. S. tax liabilities because foreign income taxes are often disguised royalty payments to foreign governments.

## Points to Consider:

1. Royalty payments to foreign governments are comparable to domestic royalty payments. In the U. S., a royalty of one-eighth, or 12½ per cent, is considered normal. The preponderance of foreign nations also collect a royalty of 12½ per cent or more. In addition, each of the foreign nations imposes an income tax. Just as in the U. S., the royalty and tax payments are distinctly different, and there is no basis for the statement that foreign income taxes are royalties.

2. The determination of whether a payment is a royalty or an income tax is not left to either the taxpayer or the foreign government. This determination is made objectively by the Internal Revenue Service after consideration of the particular circumstances of the case.

# DOUBLE DEDUCTION

## The Criticism:

The option to deduct intangible drilling costs in addition to percentage depletion constitutes an unwarranted "double deduction."

## Points to Consider:

1. Deductions for intangible drilling costs and deductions for depletion are two entirely different matters. Intangible drilling costs represent certain classes of costs incurred in drilling wells, and the income tax deductions for intangibles may never exceed the actual amounts incurred. On the other hand, depletion represents a deduction for exhaustion of a taxpayer's interest in a mineral property. Under the percentage depletion provisions, deductions can and do exceed the actual costs incurred in acquiring the mineral property, but the depletion deduction is not related to the intangible drilling costs except that such intangibles must be deducted in computing net income for each property for the purpose of determining the 50 per cent of net income limitation on percentage depletion.

2. The "double deduction" criticism is fallacious but has probably resulted from the fact that percentage depletion permits deductions in excess of actual costs incurred. This is, however, precisely the result intended by Congress. The original "discovery value" provisions as well as percentage depletion were conceived for the purpose of providing an incentive for investment of risk capital in the search for new mineral resources. Under this incentive, America has led the world in energy consumption and in industrial productivity; petroleum prices have been remarkably low; profits of oil companies have been reasonable; and a tremendous source of tax revenue has been created.

# Appendix B

# Legislative History
# of Percentage Depletion
# for Oil and Gas Production

# LEGISLATIVE HISTORY
## OF PERCENTAGE DEPLETION
## FOR OIL AND GAS PRODUCTION

In framing legislation to implement the first income tax law under the Sixteenth Amendment—the Revenue Act of 1913—Congress found that defining "income" was a problem. It was fairly easy to determine what constituted the income of a salaried worker or wage earner, but in other cases complications arose. The extractive industries, such as coal mining, metal mining, and oil and gas production, presented a problem. The basic problem was one of distinguishing between capital and income in computing the tax, and one of the most important aspects of the problem related to depletion—the gradual exhaustion of the resource as the well or mine was operated.

## Early Depletion Legislation

The first efforts of Congress to solve this capital-income difficulty were made in connection with the Revenue Act of 1913 which granted taxpayers in the extractive industries ". . . a reasonable allowance for depletion of ores and all other natural deposits" in computing their income tax, and limited the deduction to 5 per cent of the gross value of the production for the year. The deduction during the life of the property was not to be greater than the original cost of the property, or the market value as of March 1, 1913.

In the Revenue Act of 1916, Congress changed the 5 per cent limitation in the case of oil and gas wells to "a reasonable allowance for actual reduction in flow." The capital to be recovered was not to exceed the larger of the "capital originally invested" or the March 1, 1913 "fair market value." To compute the depletion deduction, it was necessary to estimate the amount of oil remaining in a property, divide this estimate into the larger of the two capital measures, and multiply by the number of barrels produced during the taxable year. For example, if the capital to be recovered for a given property was $50,000, and if it was estimated that 100,000 barrels remained to be recovered from it, the depletion deduction would be $0.50 per barrel of oil produced. If production for a year was 2,500 barrels, the depletion deduction would be $0.50 x 2,500, or $1,250. This amount was simply a return of capital, and not income.

The fair market value of an oil property very often has no relation to its original cost. A resource discovered in the earth may have, or can acquire, value far in excess of the cost of its discovery. The total discovery cost of a wildcat well, for example, might be $100,000, but its actual value once discovered could be many times that amount, and the discoverer could actually sell the property for the higher amount if he did not wish to operate it.

Tax inequities naturally resulted from the 1916 provisions because depletion on a property that was productive as of March 1, 1913 was computed on its value as of that date, whereas depletion on a property which became productive after that date was determined on cost. Before World War I, when the corporate income tax rate did not exceed 2 per cent, the disparity between the tax treatment of individual properties did not produce significant differences in results, but this situation changed with the advent of high income tax rates after the United States entered World War I.

## The Discovery Depletion Principle

The Revenue Act of 1918 took this disparity into account and extended the application of fair market value as a basis for depletion to newly discovered oil wells, gas wells, and mines. Thus, a producer who discovered a property after March 1, 1913, was put on an equal tax footing with those who had made discoveries before that date. He was enabled, in other words, to compute depletion on the discovery value of his property. Discovery value was defined as the amount of money the producer could obtain were he to sell his property within thirty days after discovery. He could then use this figure in computing that part of the revenue from the property which represented a diminution, or depletion, of his capital.

Though discovery depletion continued to be approved by several successive Congresses, its provisions proved difficult to administer. The Bureau of Internal Revenue was the scene of endless controversies over the determination of "fair market value" of every mine, oil well, or gas well within thirty days after discovery. This was often a difficult and expensive task, entailing complicated engineering analyses, frequent differences of opinion between owners and the government, and long delays in settling tax cases. The whole situation aroused so much dissatisfaction that a Select Senate Committee was appointed to study the matter.

The Committee confirmed that the law was difficult to administer. But experience had shown that the discovery value per barrel of oil, as established by appraisal of individual properties, bore a reasonably consistent relationship to the price of crude oil at the well as it was produced. It seemed, therefore, that the whole procedure of fixing a proper depletion allowance could be simplified by allowing depletion on the basis of a fixed percentage of the gross income obtained from the oil drawn out of the earth. Early in 1926 the Committee reported its findings and proposed such a substitute for discovery depletion.

## Percentage Depletion

After receiving the Select Committee proposal, the Senate Finance Committee made a study of the problem and presented a report to the Senate recommending the adoption of "percentage depletion" in the following words:

> The administration of the discovery provision of existing law in the case of oil and gas wells has been very difficult because of the discovery valuation that had to be made in the case of each discovered well. In the interest of simplicity and certainty in administration, your committee recommends that in the case of oil and gas wells the allowance for depletion shall be 25 per cent of the gross income from the property during the taxable year.

Senator Reed of Pennsylvania, in supporting the subsequent bill, observed that 25 per cent represented an average of actual experience with oil properties and that it would achieve about the same results as discovery value depletion without the guesswork involved in the latter. "If there is any error in the 25 per cent figure," he said, "it is in favor of the government." He then went on to discuss the problem:

> We provide that the owner of an oil well or a mine who is exhausting his capital when he takes out the mineral can chalk off an allowance for depletion of his property. That sounds simple; but when we come to apply that, the application is so complicated that it causes a large part of the disagreement between the taxpayers and the bureau. If Senators will think for a moment about the application of that rule to an oil well, it will be realized that the owner of the well is exhausting his capital every time he draws a barrel of oil out of the well, so part of the value of that oil is in there and part of it is a mere return of his capital. In order to calculate what part of it he can charge off to depletion, the bureau has been estimating the quantity of oil in the property, which is just about as hard as estimating the quantity of air over the

property. Then, on top of that estimate, they try to estimate what that oil will be worth in the market in future years, which multiplies the first uncertainty by a second uncertainty, and, of course, no two people ever agree on that . . . We have taken a big step forward in this bill, in our committee amendment, which provides that an arbitrary percentage of the gross selling value of that oil shall be deducted to allow for depletion. The owners of some of the oil wells say that we have not allowed enough, and some of the experts of the bureau say they think perhaps we have allowed a little too much. Probably we have been reasonably fair. But the whole thing is in the line of simplification, getting rid of this everlasting accounting.

The percentage figure was discussed at some length in the Senate. Senator Neely of West Virginia thought it necessary to increase the rate to 35 per cent in order to protect the small operator, and Senator Goff of the same state introduced an amendment providing for either a 35 or 40 per cent deduction depending on the relation of operating expenses to gross income during the taxable year. Both proposals were defeated, and a 30 per cent figure was agreed upon when the Senate adopted the bill.

The House Ways and Means Committee had agreed to recommend 25 per cent of gross income as a proper depletion deduction for oil and gas, and the compromise figure of 27½ per cent was finally established by the House and Senate Committees in conference. By the Revenue Act of 1926, then, percentage depletion at 27½ per cent was substituted for discovery depletion and made retroactive to January 1, 1925. Like discovery depletion, it applied to oil and gas production of United States taxpayers wherever their operations were conducted, whether in the United States or elsewhere. Though subject to constant review and suggested change, percentage depletion for oil and gas production has remained in effect at that figure ever since.

Fundamentally, percentage depletion is not a departure from the discovery value depletion provision of the Revenue Act of 1918. The main difference between them is in the technique of calculating the amount of the deduction. Under discovery value the deduction is based on the appraised value of the estimated reserves of oil at the time of discovery, but under percentage depletion it is based on the wellhead value of the oil as it is produced.

The current average price being paid for proved undeveloped reserves is about $0.93 a barrel, and the average wellhead price of crude oil today is about $2.88 a barrel. At that price, the maximum percentage depletion deduction at 27½ per cent is about $0.79, which is lower than the going price of undeveloped reserves. (In actual practice the depletion deduction on many properties would be less than $0.79 because it is limited to 50 per cent of net income.) It would appear, therefore, that percentage depletion recovers somewhat less than the capital value that would be recovered under discovery value depletion.

## The Limitation to 50 Per Cent of Net Income

The Revenue Act of 1921 provided that the depletion deduction should not exceed the net income from the property before deducting depletion. For example, if the net income from a well was $25,000 before depletion, and the depletion, figured on the value of the property at the time it was discovered, came to $40,000, the taxpayer could not take more than $25,000 as his depletion deduction for the year. In its report, the Senate Finance Committee urged this limitation ". . . in order to make certain that the depletion deduction when based upon discovery value shall not be permitted to offset or cancel profits derived by the taxpayer from a separate and distinct line of business."

In 1921, the Treasury Department had strongly recommended that the discovery depletion deduction be limited to 50 per cent of the net income from the property, and in the Revenue Act of 1924 this proposal was adopted. Thus, beginning in 1924 the taxpayer in the above example was required to reduce his depletion deduction to $12,500—that is, 50 per cent of his net income.

Once depletion was limited to 50 per cent of the income from *the property*, the definition of that term (the property) became of major significance. Because the term had been used in more than one way in the Regulations, the Revenue Service in 1941, and again in 1944, issued a memorandum defining *the property* as ". . . each separate interest owned by the taxpayer in each separate tract or parcel of land." However, so long as they were consistent, taxpayers were permitted to combine two or more mineral deposits found in a single tract of land and to treat this combination of interests as a single property. All interests in the tract not so combined had to be treated as separate properties.

In 1954 the Code was amended to permit one aggregation of properties within each "operating unit." These aggregation provisions, however, were revoked in 1964 for oil and gas producers, so that the Code now provides for the determination of "the property" in the computation of percentage depletion by substantially the same method as before 1954.

# Depletion Provisions Unchanged

Except for these modifications in the definition of the term "the property" as applied to the 50 per cent limitation, the percentage depletion provisions for oil and gas have remained substantially intact since 1926. The Revenue Act of 1928 introduced minor technical revisions in the way the depletion deduction should be apportioned, and the Act of 1932 extended percentage depletion to metal, sulfur, and coal mines. Neither, however, made any significant change in the petroleum provisions of the 1926 Act. The Revenue Acts of 1934, 1936, 1938, and 1939 made no changes.

During these years, however, percentage depletion was debated at great length. Congress has considered many proposals for revising the percentage depletion provisions for oil and gas, but on each occasion, after exhaustive hearings and study, Congress has concluded that neither the principle nor the rate of percentage depletion for oil and gas should be changed.

The basic discovery value principle of depletion still stands today. In effect, it represents a decision by Congress as to what constitutes capital and what constitutes income in the extractive industries. Over the life of a property which produces oil or another mineral resource, the tax deductions may exceed the historical cost. Only in this manner can taxation on the capital value created by discovery be avoided. Although Congress has reconsidered its decision many times it has adhered to this policy for over forty years.

Additional copies of this booklet
may be secured
from
Mid-Continent Oil & Gas Association
300 Tulsa Building
Tulsa, Oklahoma 74103